Grade 4

Unit Resource Guide
Unit 15
Using Patterns

SECOND EDITION

A Mathematical Journey Using Science and Language Arts

KENDALL/HUNT PUBLISHING COMPANY
4050 Westmark Drive   Dubuque, Iowa 52002

A TIMS® Curriculum
University of Illinois at Chicago

UIC The University of Illinois at Chicago

The original edition was based on work supported by the National Science Foundation under grant No. MDR 9050226 and the University of Illinois at Chicago. Any opinions, findings, and conclusions or recommendations expressed in this publication are those of the author(s) and do not necessarily reflect the views of the granting agencies.

LETTER HOME

Using Patterns

Date: _____

Dear Family Member:

Your child will look for patterns in data and use these patterns to make predictions. For example, the class has been recording the heights of growing plants for a few weeks. In this unit, we will display the plant data in a graph and use the shape of the graph to predict what the general growth pattern is for plants.

Your child will also identify, describe, and use number patterns. We will use an imaginary planet called Gzorp, where all creatures are made of square "cells." Children imagine that new squares are added to Gzorp creatures every year, according to some pattern. Your child will find the pattern for different Gzorp creatures, then predict what that creature will look like at certain ages.

Number patterns created by special "function machines" will also be studied. Your child will use machines such as the "doubler" to predict what happens when a number is entered into the machine. The class will also study patterns in data by conducting a laboratory investigation with mass. Your child will find the mass of a sandwich in the *Taste of TIMS* lab. Please have your child bring a sandwich to school when we begin this investigation.

A three- and four-year-old
Triangle Fish from Planet Gzorp

Our work with patterns will develop students' mathematical reasoning and prepare them for the formal study of algebra. You can help your child at home by doing the following:

- **Look at Graphs.** Encourage your child to look for graphs in newspapers and magazines. Then, have him or her describe the graph and explain what the graph tells you.

- **Play *Guess My Rule.*** Your child will learn to play this game at school. Ask your child to teach you this game at home. Refer to the rules listed in the *Student Guide*.

- **Math Facts.** Help your child use the *Triangle Flash Cards* to review the division facts for the threes and nines. Students also review the twelve division facts related to the "last six" multiplication facts ($24 \div 4$, $24 \div 6$, $28 \div 4$, $28 \div 7$, $32 \div 4$, $32 \div 8$, $42 \div 6$, $42 \div 7$, $48 \div 6$, $48 \div 8$, $56 \div 7$, $56 \div 8$).

Sincerely,

_____

UNIT OUTLINE

Using Patterns

Pacing Suggestions

The laboratory investigations and the *Adventure Book* story in this unit make strong connections to science. Use science time to collect data for these labs.

- Lesson 1 concludes the *Plant Growth* lab begun in Unit 13. Students should begin this lesson when the growth of their plants has leveled off. This is usually about 20 days after the seeds have sprouted.

- Lesson 2 *In the Shade of the Old Meranpi Tree* is an optional lesson. It is appropriate to read this story as part of science or language arts after completing Lesson 1.

- Lesson 3 *Planet Gzorp* introduces students to a context for investigating numerical patterns. This context is used again in the open-response assessment problem in Unit 16 Lesson 4. Students can complete this assessment in Unit 16 anytime after completing Lesson 3 of this unit.

- Lesson 5 *Taste of TIMS* includes *Mass Review,* an optional activity in the *Unit Resource Guide,* for those students who have not had previous experiences measuring mass.

- Lesson 6 *Patterns and Problems* is an optional lesson. It is a set of word problems that students can complete in class or for homework.

Components Key: SG = Student Guide, DAB = Discovery Assignment Book, AB = Adventure Book, URG = Unit Resource Guide, and DPP = Daily Practice and Problems

	Sessions	Description	Supplies
LESSON 1 **Plant Growth Conclusion** SG pages 402–405 DAB page 243 URG pages 22–33 DPP A–D	2	**LAB:** Students use the data they began collecting in Unit 13 Lesson 5 to generate a graph, explore its characteristics, and answer discussion questions.	• calculators
LESSON 2 **In the Shade of the Old Meranpi Tree** AB pages 91–106 URG pages 34–42	– OPTIONAL LESSON –		
	1	**OPTIONAL ADVENTURE BOOK:** Dr. Clark and her son travel to Borneo to study the effects of gap cutting on the rain forest. They find a relationship between the area of the gap and its ability to regenerate meranpi trees.	

	Sessions	Description	Supplies
LESSON 3 **Planet Gzorp** SG pages 406–410 URG pages 43–57 DPP E–H	2	**ACTIVITY:** Students describe number patterns in the context of an imaginary planet, Gzorp, where creatures are made of squares. **ASSESSMENT PAGE:** *Make Your Own*, Unit Resource Guide, pages 54–55.	• calculators • square-inch tiles
LESSON 4 **Function Machines** SG pages 411–416 URG pages 58–67 DPP I–L	2–3	**ACTIVITY:** Students are introduced to function machines and play the game *Guess My Rule.*	• calculators
LESSON 5 **Taste of TIMS** SG pages 417–423 URG pages 68–82 DPP M–P	2–3	**LAB:** Students find the mass of a sandwich. Then, they take a bite and find the mass again. Students find the relationship between the mass of the sandwich and the number of bites they take. This decreasing relationship is plotted on a graph.	• two-pan balances • standard masses • napkins, plastic wrap, or wax paper • sandwiches • calculators
LESSON 6 **Patterns and Problems** SG pages 424–427 URG pages 83–86	1–2	– OPTIONAL LESSON – **OPTIONAL ACTIVITY:** Students solve problems based on concepts learned in the unit.	• calculators

A current list of connections is available at www.mathtrailblazers.com.

Literature

Suggested Titles

- Baptista, Lynne Hardie. *Discover Rain Forests.* Publications International, Ltd., Lincolnwood, IL, 1993.
- Cherry, Lynne. *The Great Kapok Tree: A Tale of the Amazon Rain Forest.* Voyager Books, New York, 2000.
- Jordan, Martin and Janis. *Journey of the Red-Eyed Tree Frog.* Simon & Schuster, New York, 1992.
- Perez, Ed. *A Look Around Rain Forests.* Willowisp Press, Inc., St. Petersburg, FL, 1993.

Software

- *Building Perspective* develops spatial reasoning and visual thinking in three dimensions.
- *The Factory Deluxe* promotes spatial reasoning and provides practice with finding area.
- *A Field Trip to the Rain Forest Deluxe* integrates mathematics with science.
- *The Logical Journey of the Zoombinis* provides practice with finding patterns to solve puzzles.
- *Math Arena* is a collection of math activities that reinforces many math concepts.
- *Math Workshop Deluxe* provides practice with fractions and decimals and develops spatial sense and math facts proficiency.
- *National Library of Virtual Manipulatives* website (http://matti.usu.edu) allows students to work with number patterns and number puzzles.
- *Number Sense–Puzzle Tanks* develops logical thinking while practicing math facts.
- *Schoolhouse Rock!* provides practice with number sense, math facts, and geometry skills.
- *Shape Up!* provides activities with 5 different sets of shapes.

PREPARING FOR UPCOMING LESSONS

In Lesson 5 *Taste of TIMS,* students will find the mass of sandwiches. Ask students to bring in a sandwich for this lab. Refer to Lesson 5, Before the Lab, for a description of appropriate sandwiches.

Using Patterns

> "Change is an important mathematical idea that can be studied using the tools of algebra. For example, as part of a science project, students might plant seeds and record the growth of a plant. Using data represented in the table and graph . . ., students can describe how the rate of growth varies over time."
>
> From the National Council of Teachers of Mathematics "Algebra Standards for Grades 3–5" in *Principles and Standards for School Mathematics,* 2000.

In this unit students will explore, analyze, and extend patterns. Each activity promotes students' mathematical reasoning and prepares students for the formal study of algebra. While real world data may not fit an exact mathematical pattern, many situations give rise to patterns that are close to mathematical patterns, and we use these patterns to make the best possible predictions.

The first activity involves studying the plant growth data students began to collect in Unit 13. While each student will have different data, there will be certain patterns that are common to many plants. For example, students will discover that plants grow slowly when they first germinate. As plants get older, they grow at a faster, constant rate (about the same number of centimeters each day). Finally, as a plant reaches its mature height, its growth slows down, and it may finally cease to grow (taller).

Students also find, describe, and use number patterns to solve problems in the context of an imaginary planet called Gzorp. The creatures on Gzorp are made of squares and grow according to certain exact patterns. See Figure 1.

Counting the number of squares in a creature every "year" gives rise to a variety of patterns. Students find this to be an engaging context in which they develop their skills at recognizing patterns, describing patterns, and using patterns to make predictions. Students extend the growth patterns and find out how many squares each creature has at certain ages. This activity differs from *Plant Growth* in that the patterns are exact numerical patterns without experimental error.

Students use "function machines" to explore relationships in data. Function machines alter numbers according to a fixed rule or pattern. Each machine takes a number called the "input," changes it according to its rule, and emits a new number as its "output." For example, the doubling machine outputs the number that is two times the input number. Work with these machines serves several purposes. At the most basic level, they help students reinforce and extend their experiences with the four operations. More importantly, the lessons deal with recognizing and describing numerical patterns. These concepts are important building blocks for the understanding of algebra. See the TIMS Tutor: *Functions* in the *Teacher Implementation Guide* for more information on this topic.

Figure 1: *Three-year-old and four-year-old Triangle Fish from planet Gzorp*

The *Taste of TIMS* lab provides a practical example of patterns in the real world while investigating the concept of mass. Students find the mass of a sandwich and see how the mass changes when one bite, and then additional bites, are taken from the sandwich. This laboratory investigation serves as an assessment of your students' abilities to use the TIMS Laboratory Method. However, students should be encouraged to use their own approaches whenever they are applicable. There is much to be learned from providing students with opportunities to make reasonable problem-solving decisions of their own. For more information on mass or the TIMS Laboratory Method, see the TIMS Tutors: *The Concept of Mass* and *The TIMS Laboratory Method* in the *Teacher Implementation Guide.*

Notes on Graphing

The graphing techniques in this unit are an integral part of *Math Trailblazers*™ and are powerful tools for studying many of the big ideas students will encounter in their study of mathematics. In this unit, students graph data in point graphs. In most cases there is a pattern in the data points. Drawing a line or a curve on the graph is one way to show the pattern. The line or curve can be used for making predictions about values that lie between and beyond the data points. One common pattern that we study frequently is an increasing straight line. An example is shown in Graph A in Figure 2. We have seen many examples of these lines in previous units (i.e., *Bouncing Ball, Volume vs. Number, Downhill Racer,* etc.). Another important example is the line that is decreasing as shown in Graph B. A good example of this type of line is the graph in the *Taste of TIMS* lab, where the mass of a sandwich decreases as bites are taken out of it. Other graphs have more complex shapes; for example, the growth curve in the *Plant Growth* experiment as shown in Graph C.

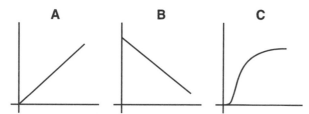

Figure 2: *Examples of graphs: (A) increasing, straight line; (B) decreasing, straight line; (C) growth curve*

For more information about graphing, see the TIMS Tutor: *The TIMS Laboratory Method* in the *Teacher Implementation Guide.*

Notes on Functions

Mathematicians have several definitions for the concept of function. Since it does not make sense to discuss these definitions with young children, we merely say that a **function** is a rule that for every input number gives you exactly one output number. The four major ways of describing functions follow.

- In words: Some examples of rules for functions are "doubling," "add ten," "multiply by four and add ten," "square the number," and "multiply the number by itself." Note that the last two examples are the same.

- In symbols: A common way to define a function is to represent the input number by a letter. The rule for the output can then be written using symbols. If N represents the input number, the functions written in words above can be written in symbols as $2 \times N$, $N + 10$, and $4 \times N + 10$, N^2, and $N \times N$, respectively.

- In data tables: Figure 3 shows an input/output data table for a function.

Input	Output
0	0
1	2
2	4
3	6
4	8
5	10

Figure 3: *An input/output table*

It is not difficult to see that the data table in Figure 3 is for the doubling function. We can describe this function in words, "The output number is double the input number" and in symbols, "$N \times 2$." One of the important processes in science, technology, and mathematics is collecting data, organizing it in a data table, and then finding the pattern that describes the relation between input and output. Data tables are of limited use, however, since we could never complete a data table that included *all* numbers.

- In graphs: For each of the examples given above, plotting data points represents the pattern visually.

While a graph and a data table are very useful ways to represent functions, they are not completely satisfactory since they do not contain all the information about the function. Any graph will contain only a limited range of values. On the other hand, graphs and data tables are powerful tools for finding patterns and solving problems. Graphs, in particular, allow us to use our visual capabilities as a very powerful tool for understanding and discovering patterns.

Mathematicians and scientists describe functions using symbols, for example, $y = x^3 + 1$. Giving students early, concrete experiences with functions will help them understand the abstract work with symbols they will encounter in later grades.

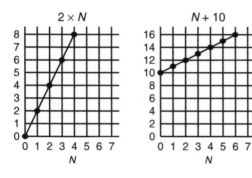

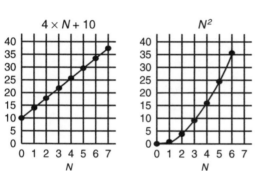

Figure 4: *Example graphs*

Resources

Principles and Standards for School Mathematics. National Council of Teachers of Mathematics, Reston, VA, 2000.

Assessment Indicators

- Can students collect, organize, graph, and analyze data?
- Can students make and interpret point graphs?
- Can students draw and interpret best-fit lines?
- Can students identify and extend patterns?
- Can students use patterns to make predictions?
- Can students represent patterns and functions using words, symbols, tables, and graphs?
- Can students identify and use variables?
- Can students measure mass?
- Do students show fluency with the division facts for the 3s, 9s, and the 12 division facts related to the last six facts ($24 \div 4$, $24 \div 6$, $28 \div 4$, $28 \div 7$, $32 \div 4$, $32 \div 8$, $42 \div 6$, $42 \div 7$, $48 \div 6$, $48 \div 8$, $56 \div 7$, $56 \div 8$)?

OBSERVATIONAL ASSESSMENT RECORD

(A1) Can students collect, organize, graph, and analyze data?

(A2) Can students make and interpret point graphs?

(A3) Can students draw and interpret best-fit lines?

(A4) Can students identify and extend patterns?

(A5) Can students use patterns to make predictions?

(A6) Can students represent patterns and functions using words, symbols, tables, and graphs?

(A7) Can students identify and use variables?

(A8) Can students measure mass?

(A9) Do students show fluency with the division facts for the 3s, 9s, and the 12 division facts related to the last six facts ($24 \div 4$, $24 \div 6$, $28 \div 4$, $28 \div 7$, $32 \div 4$, $32 \div 8$, $42 \div 6$, $42 \div 7$, $48 \div 6$, $48 \div 8$, $56 \div 7$, $56 \div 8$)?

(A10) _____

Name	A1	A2	A3	A4	A5	A6	A7	A8	A9	A10	Comments
1.											
2.											
3.											
4.											
5.											
6.											
7.											
8.											
9.											
10.											
11.											
12.											
13.											

Name	A1	A2	A3	A4	A5	A6	A7	A8	A9	A10	Comments
14.											
15.											
16.											
17.											
18.											
19.											
20.											
21.											
22.											
23.											
24.											
25.											
26.											
27.											
28.											
29.											
30.											
31.											
32.											

Using Patterns

Two Daily Practice and Problems (DPP) items are included for each class session listed in the Unit Outline. The first item is always a Bit and the second is either a Task or a Challenge. Refer to the Daily Practice and Problems and Home Practice Guide in the *Teacher Implementation Guide* for further information on the DPP. A Scope and Sequence Chart for the Daily Practice and Problems for the year can be found in the Scope and Sequence Chart & the NCTM *Principles and Standards* section of the *Teacher Implementation Guide*.

A DPP Menu for Unit 15

Eight icons designate the subject matter of the DPP items. Each DPP item falls into one or more of the categories listed below. A brief menu of the DPP items included in Unit 15 follows.

N Number Sense A, F, H–J, L, N	**Computation** D, E, H	**Time** C	**Geometry** C, P
Math Facts B, E, G, J, L, M, O	**$ Money**	**Measurement** I, P	**Data** A, K

Practice and Assessment of the Division Facts

The DPP for this unit continues the systematic strategies-based approach to learning the division facts. This unit reviews the threes, nines, and 12 related division facts for the last six multiplication facts (4×6, 4×7, 4×8, 6×7, 6×8, 7×8). The *Triangle Flash Cards* for these groups can be found in the *Unit Resource Guide* Generic Section and the *Grade 4 Facts Resource Guide*. The cards for the five groups were first distributed in the *Discovery Assignment Book* in Units 3–8 and 10–13, following the Home Practice. A discussion of the flash cards and how to use them can be found in item B of the DPP. Practice of the division facts is provided in items E, G, and L. Two quizzes on the facts are provided in items M and O.

For more information about the distribution and assessment of the math facts, see the TIMS Tutor: *Math Facts* in the *Teacher Implementation Guide*. Also refer to the DPP guides in the *Unit Resource Guide* for Units 3 and 9.

Students may solve the items individually, in groups, or as a class. The items may also be assigned for homework.

Student Questions	Teacher Notes
A **Plant Growth**	**TIMS Bit**
1. In Ms. Meyer's class, students planted a total of 100 seeds out of a large bag of sunflower seeds. Eighty seeds sprouted. What fraction of the seeds that the students planted sprouted?	1. $\frac{80}{100}$ (or $\frac{8}{10}$, 0.8, or $\frac{4}{5}$) 2. $\frac{80}{100}$ (or $\frac{8}{10}$ or $\frac{4}{5}$)
2. What is the probability that a sunflower seed in Ms. Meyer's bag of seeds will sprout?	

Division Facts

With a partner, use your *Triangle Flash Cards* to quiz each other on the division facts for the threes, nines, and the 12 related division facts for the last six multiplication facts (4 × 6, 4 × 7, 4 × 8, 6 × 7, 6 × 8, 7 × 8). One partner covers the corner with a square with his or her thumb. This number will be the answer to a division fact, called the quotient. The second person divides the two uncovered numbers. Repeat the process, this time covering the corner with a circle.

Each time through the cards, separate them into three piles: those facts you know and can answer quickly, those that you can figure out with a strategy, and those that you need to learn. Practice the last two piles again and then make a list of the facts you need to practice at home for homework.

Circle the facts you know and can answer quickly on your *Division Facts I Know* chart.

TIMS Task

For those students who need new copies of the *Triangle Flash Cards*, masters for the flash cards can be found in the *Unit Resource Guide* Generic Section. After students sort the cards, they should be encouraged to practice the facts in the last two piles—those facts that they can figure out with a strategy and those they need to learn. Discuss strategies students use to find the answers to the facts, emphasizing those strategies that are more efficient than others.

Sstudents make a list of the facts they need to practice at home for homework as well as update their *Division Facts I Know* charts. In Part 1 of the Home Practice, students are reminded to bring home their *Triangle Flash Cards*.

Inform students when the two quizzes on the facts will be. Half of the facts appear in item M. The others appear in item O.

Angles and Time

1. It is 3:00. How many degrees is the angle that is formed by the two hands on the clock?

2. It is 3:00. When the *minute* hand turns 90 degrees, what time will it be?

3. It is 3:00. When the *hour* hand turns 90 degrees, what time will it be?

TIMS Bit

Draw pictures of a clock or use a clock for illustration purposes as necessary.

1. 90 degrees

2. 3:15

3. 6:00

 Computing Multiplication and Division

Use paper and pencil or mental math to compute the following. Estimate the answers to see if your answers are reasonable.

1. A. 33 × 74 =   B. 50 × 80 =

   C. 61 × 36 =   D. 27 × 95 =

   E. 273 ÷ 8 =   F. 1056 ÷ 6 =

2. Explain your estimation strategy for Question 1D.

TIMS Task

1. A. 2442

   B. 4000

   C. 2196

   D. 2565

   E. 34 R1

   F. 176

2. Possible strategy:
   27 × 100 = 2700

E Multiplying and Dividing by Multiples of 10

A. $500 \times 30 =$ B. $60 \times 4 =$

C. $50 \times 90 =$ D. $0 \times 300 =$

E. $2400 \div 8 =$ F. $900 \div 9 =$

G. $30 \div 10 =$ H. $1800 \div 2 =$

I. $210 \div 30 =$ J. $1200 \div 40 =$

K. $60 \times 700 =$ L. $0 \div 9 =$

TIMS Bit

A. 15,000

B. 240

C. 4500

D. 0

E. 300

F. 100

G. 3

H. 900

I. 7

J. 30

K. 42,000

L. 0

F Add to the Pattern

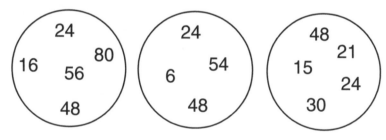

1. What do the numbers in each circle have in common? Write two more numbers that belong in each circle.

2. Why are 24 and 48 in all three circles?

TIMS Task

1. The first circle contains numbers which are multiples of 2, 4, and 8. The middle circle contains numbers that are multiples of 2, 3, and 6. The last circle contains numbers that are multiples of 3.

2. 24 and 48 are multiples of 2, 3, 4, 6, and 8.

Fact Families for × and ÷

Solve each fact. Then, name the three other facts that are in the same fact family. (The square numbers only have two facts in each family.)

A. 6 × 8 =

B. 18 ÷ 6 =

C. 81 ÷ 9 =

D. 9 × 8 =

E. 4 × 7 =

F. 3 × 2 =

G. 32 ÷ 4 =

H. 7 × 6 =

I. 9 ÷ 3 =

J. 27 ÷ 3 =

K. 9 × 1 =

TIMS Bit

Complete this item orally as a class. One student can solve the given fact and other students can name each of the other related facts.

A. 48; 8 × 6 = 48
 48 ÷ 6 = 8
 48 ÷ 8 = 6

B. 3; 18 ÷ 3 = 6
 6 × 3 = 18
 3 × 6 = 18

C. 9; 9 × 9 = 81

D. 72; 8 × 9 = 72
 72 ÷ 8 = 9
 72 ÷ 9 = 8

E. 28; 7 × 4 = 28
 28 ÷ 4 = 7
 28 ÷ 7 = 4

F. 6; 2 × 3 = 6
 6 ÷ 3 = 2
 6 ÷ 2 = 3

G. 8; 32 ÷ 8 = 4
 4 × 8 = 32
 8 × 4 = 32

H. 42; 42 ÷ 7 = 6
 42 ÷ 6 = 7
 6 × 7 = 42

I. 3; 3 × 3 = 9

J. 9; 27 ÷ 9 = 3
 3 × 9 = 27
 9 × 3 = 27

K. 9; 1 × 9 = 9
 9 ÷ 1 = 9
 9 ÷ 9 = 1

Division Practice

Use paper and pencil or mental math to compute the following. Estimate to see if your answers are reasonable.

1. 87 ÷ 3 =   2. 417 ÷ 5 =

3. 247 ÷ 6 =   4. 4916 ÷ 9 =

5. 5984 ÷ 8 =   6. 6078 ÷ 7 =

TIMS Task

1. 29
2. 83 R2
3. 41 R1
4. 546 R2
5. 748
6. 868 R2

 Find the Pattern

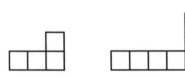 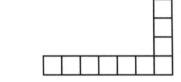

1. Draw the next two shapes on *Centimeter Grid Paper.*

2. How many square centimeters will there be in each shape?

TIMS Bit

1.

2. 13 sq cm, 16 sq cm

Function Machine: Order of Operations

Complete the following table. Make sure you follow the correct order of operations.

Input	Output
1	
2	
3	
4	
5	
6	
7	
N	$10 + 3 \times N$

TIMS Task

You may need to remind students to multiply the input number by 3 before adding 10.

Input	Output
1	13
2	16
3	19
4	22
5	25
6	28
7	31
N	$10 + 3 \times N$

 Planet Gzorp

On Planet Gzorp there is a family of six L-gators. The three female L-gators are 3 years old, 14 years old, and 29 years old. The three males are 9, 18, and 41 years old.

1. What is the mean age of the members of this family of L-gators?

2. What is the median age?

TIMS Bit

1. 19 years old

2. 16 years old

Student Questions	Teacher Notes

 Related Multiplication and Division Sentences

Find a number for *n* in each number sentence that makes the statement true.

1. $4 \times n = 2400$ $2400 \div 4 = n$

2. $n \times 9 = 360$ $360 \div 9 = n$

3. $7 \times n = 63{,}000$ $63{,}000 \div 7 = n$

4. $6 \times n = 54$ $54 \div 6 = n$

5. $9 \times n = 4500$ $4500 \div 9 = n$

6. $8 \times n = 560$ $560 \div 8 = n$

7. $3 \times n = 0$ $0 \div 3 = n$

TIMS Task

1. $n = 600$
2. $n = 40$
3. $n = 9000$
4. $n = 9$
5. $n = 500$
6. $n = 70$
7. $n = 0$

Ⓜ Division Facts Quiz 1

A. $90 \div 9 =$ B. $6 \div 3 =$

C. $3 \div 3 =$ D. $48 \div 8 =$

E. $15 \div 5 =$ F. $63 \div 7 =$

G. $32 \div 4 =$ H. $18 \div 9 =$

I. $9 \div 3 =$ J. $9 \div 1 =$

K. $36 \div 4 =$ L. $42 \div 7 =$

M. $54 \div 9 =$ N. $24 \div 3 =$

TIMS Bit

This quiz is on the division facts for the threes, nines, and last six facts. Half of the facts are on this quiz. Half appear in the quiz in Bit O. We recommend 2 minutes for this quiz. Allow students to change pens after the time is up and complete the remaining problems in a different color.

After students take the quiz, have them update their *Division Facts I Know* charts. It is likely that the student who knows $90 \div 9$ also knows $90 \div 10$. To make sure, ask students to write the related division fact for each fact on the quiz (except the square numbers). A student who answers a given fact correctly and who also writes the related division fact correctly can circle both facts on the chart.

Student Questions	Teacher Notes

 Clean It Up!

Frank found a function machine that was so dirty that he couldn't read its rule. He recorded some of the inputs and outputs, but his paper got smudged. Complete Frank's data table. Then, tell the rule for the function machine.

Input	Output
29	2900
■	8000
1290	■
513	51,300

TIMS Task

The missing input is 80. The missing output is 129,000. The rule is "multiply by 100."

O Division Facts Quiz 2

A. $27 \div 9 =$ B. $28 \div 7 =$

C. $12 \div 3 =$ D. $24 \div 6 =$

E. $56 \div 8 =$ F. $81 \div 9 =$

G. $21 \div 3 =$ H. $30 \div 10 =$

I. $45 \div 9 =$ J. $72 \div 9 =$

K. $24 \div 3 =$ L. $3 \div 3 =$

M. $0 \div 9 =$ N. $18 \div 3 =$

TIMS Bit

This quiz is on the division facts for the threes, nines, and last six facts. Half of the facts are on this quiz. Half were in the quiz in Bit M. We recommend 2 minutes for this quiz. Allow students to change pens after the time is up and complete the remaining problems in a different color.

After students take the quiz, have them update their *Division Facts I Know* charts. It is likely that the student who knows $27 \div 9$ also knows $27 \div 3$. To make sure, ask students to write the related division fact for each fact on the quiz (except the square numbers). A student who answers a given fact correctly and who also writes the related division fact correctly can circle both facts on the chart.

Drawing Angles

You will need a protractor to complete the following problems.

1. Draw ∠RTG with a measurement of 35°.

2. Draw ∠MQF with a measurement of 115°.

3. Draw ∠GWP with a measurement of 78°.

TIMS Task

1.

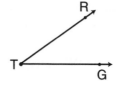

2.

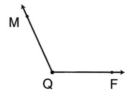

3.

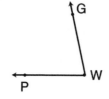

A. Plant Growth (URG p. 12)

1. In Ms. Meyer's class, students planted a total of 100 seeds out of a large bag of sunflower seeds. Eighty seeds sprouted. What fraction of the seeds that the students planted sprouted?

2. What is the probability that a sunflower seed in Ms. Meyer's bag of seeds will sprout?

C. Angles and Time (URG p. 14)

1. It is 3:00. How many degrees is the angle that is formed by the two hands on the clock?

2. It is 3:00. When the *minute* hand turns 90 degrees, what time will it be?

3. It is 3:00. When the *hour* hand turns 90 degrees, what time will it be?

DPP Tasks are on page 28. Suggestions for using the DPPs are on page 28.

LESSON GUIDE

Plant Growth Conclusion

Estimated Class Sessions: 2

Students analyze the plant growth data for the plants they started growing in Unit 13 Lesson 5. They graph their data and describe the "story of the graph." Students share their graphs with the class and compare the stories they tell using their plant growth graphs.

Key Content

- Collecting, organizing, graphing, and analyzing data.
- Measuring length in centimeters.
- Making and interpreting point graphs.
- Investigating how a change in one variable relates to a change in a second variable.
- Identifying and describing situations with varying rates of change.
- Using data to make predictions.
- Connecting mathematics and science to real-world events: measuring plant growth.

Materials List

	Math Facts and Daily Practice and Problems	Lab	Homework
Student Guide (Student Books)		*Plant Growth Conclusion* Pages 402–404 and Student Rubric: *Telling* Appendix C and Inside Back Cover	*Plant Growth* Homework Section Pages 404–405
Discovery Assignment Book		*Good and Bad Experiments* Page 243 (optional)	Home Practice Parts 1 & 2 Page 239
Facts Resource Guide (Teacher Resources)	DPP Item 15B Use the *Triangle Flash Cards* for the *3s, 9s,* and *Last Six Facts* to practice the division facts for these groups.		
Unit Resource Guide	DPP Items A–D Pages 12–14		
Generic Section		*Centimeter Graph Paper,* 2 per student and *Two-column Data Table,* 1 per student	*Triangle Flash Cards: 3s, 9s,* and *Last Six Facts,* 1 each per student (optional)

available on Teacher Resource CD

All Transparency Masters, Blackline Masters, and Assessment Blackline Masters in the Unit Resource Guide are on the Teacher Resource CD.

Supplies for Each Student

calculator

Materials for the Teacher

Transparency of *Two-column Data Table* (Unit Resource Guide, Generic Section)
Observational Assessment Record (Unit Resource Guide, Pages 9–10 and Teacher Resource CD)
TIMS Multidimensional Rubric (Teacher Implementation Guide, Assessment section)

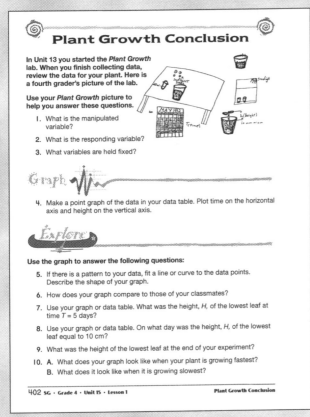

Student Guide - Page 402

Before the Lab

In Unit 13, students planted seeds and collected data on the growth of one plant. They should continue collecting the data until the growth—the height of the lowest leaf (*H*)—starts to level off. This usually takes about 20 days. At this point in the experiment, students can begin to analyze their data.

Developing the Lab

Use the sample student picture on the *Plant Growth Conclusion* Lab Pages in the *Student Guide* and *Questions 1–3* to remind students of the main variables in the *Plant Growth* lab. Ask students to refer to their own pictures of the lab as well. One variable is time, the number of days elapsed since the seed first sprouted. The other variable is the height of the first leaf, measured in centimeters. Time (*T*) is the manipulated variable, since we have decided on its values before the experiment. The responding variable is height (*H*), since we only find out height as a result of doing the experiment. The fixed variables *(Question 3)* in this experiment are the type of plant, the type of soil, the size of the container, the time of day that the plant is measured, etc.

Distribute *Centimeter Graph Paper*. Observe students as they plot their points on the graph *(Question 4)*. Note whether students have labeled both axes of their graphs with variables and the appropriate units of measure. Time in days (*T*), the manipulated variable, is plotted on the horizontal axis and height in centimeters (*H*) is plotted on the vertical axis. Each axis should be scaled appropriately and each graph should have a title. A sample data table and graph are shown in Figures 5 and 6.

Plant Growth

Date	T Time in Days	H Height in cm
5/15	0	0 cm
5/18	3	3 cm
5/19	4	5 cm
5/20	5	7 cm
5/21	6	10 cm
5/22	7	11 cm
5/26	11	12 cm
5/27	12	12.5 cm
5/28	13	13 cm
5/29	14	13.5 cm

Figure 5: *A sample student data table*

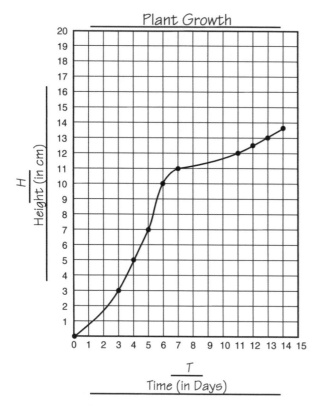

Figure 6: *A graph of the data*

Once students have plotted the data points, they are asked to fit a line or a curve through their data points *(Question 5)*. Some students will be tempted to draw a best-fit line, since many of the previous experiments have resulted in data that was close to a straight line. However, a straight line usually does not fit plant growth data. When students fit a curve, encourage them to draw a smooth curve through the points. Ask students to describe the shapes of their curves and to compare their graphs with other students' graphs *(Question 6)*. Some students may notice that most of the plants give data that lie on a curve that looks like a stretched-out "S."

In *Questions 7–9,* students use their graphs to answer questions about the growth of their plants. In *Question 10,* students should notice that the curve is steepest on the days that the plant is growing the fastest. You can see in Figure 6 that in the first three days the plant grows about 1 cm per day. Between days 3 and 6, it is growing between 2 and 3 centimeters per day. After day 6, it is again growing 1 centimeter or less each day. In general, your students' curves should have similar shapes, but the rate of growth and final height of the plants will vary.

11. Write a paragraph that tells the story of your graph. Use your answers to Question 10 to help you. Include the following information: On which days did your plant grow the most? On which days did it grow the least? How did your plant grow in the beginning, middle, and end of your experiment?

12. What do you think the data would show if you continued to record the growth of the plant?

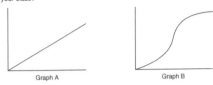

13. Which graph, Graph A or Graph B, looks more like the graphs of the plants in your class?

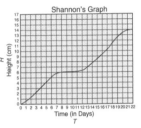

Graph A   Graph B

14. Compare your graph with some of the other graphs you have drawn this year. How are the graphs different? How are they similar?

15. Shannon and Jerome graphed the growth of their plants. What do the graphs tell you about how the plants grew? Using the graphs, tell as much as you can about how Shannon's and Jerome's plants grew. Compare the stories of the two graphs. How were they the same and how were they different?

Plant Growth Conclusion   SG · Grade 4 · Unit 15 · Lesson 1   403

Student Guide - Page 403

Content Note

Plant Growth Curves. We usually get an "S-shaped" curve in this experiment. See Figure 8. This type of curve is typical for many growing organisms.

Question 11 asks students to write a paragraph which tells the story of the graph. For example, referring to the data table and graph in Figures 7 and 8, students might say that the plant grew slowly in the first few days. Between Day 4 and Day 18 the graph is steeper which shows the plant is growing faster. The graph levels off after Day 18 which tells us that the plant is growing slower again.

Plant Growth

Date	T Time in Days	H Height in cm
10/19	0	0
10/21	2	$\frac{1}{2}$
10/23	4	1
10/26	7	6
10/28	9	10
10/30	11	12
11/2	14	16
11/4	16	18
11/6	18	19
11/9	21	19

Figure 7: *Grace's data table for Homework Questions 1–4*

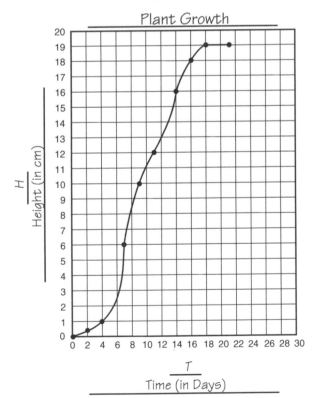

Figure 8: *Grace's graph for Homework Questions 1–4*

Question 12 asks students to make a prediction for what will happen to their plant growth data if they continue to record data for another week. Encourage students to observe the patterns in their data tables and graphs before making their predictions. Students should support their predictions with previous data. Students can verify their predictions by continuing to gather data for another week.

Using their graphs, students should be able to choose the graph in *Question 13* that looks the most like their graphs. Graph B is probably closest to theirs because a plant's growth begins to level off after a period of time.

To answer *Question 14,* students can compare their plant growth graphs with some of the other graphs they have drawn this year: *Bouncing Ball* (Unit 5 Lesson 4), the rice on a checkerboard graph (Unit 6 Lesson 2), and *Downhill Racer* (Unit 10 Lesson 4).

Encourage them to be general in their descriptions of the graphs in *Question 15.* Jerome's graph shows a typical plant growth curve whereas Shannon's does not. Her graph shows that for some reason the growth of her plant slowed down between days 7 and 12. Students might say:

- Both plants grew slowly when they were young.
- Plant growth levels off after a time; the height stays nearly the same at the end of the experiment.
- Shannon's plant stopped growing around Day 8 and then started growing again on Day 11. Jerome's plant did not stop growing until the end.

Each of these statements describes a portion of a plant's growth. Encourage students to combine them with other observations to create a full description of the pattern for plant growth.

Journal Prompt
Imagine a plant living somewhere outdoors. The graph in homework *Question 5* in the *Student Guide* is the graph of its growth over the first 21 days of its life. Write a story of how it grew.

Daily Practice and Problems:
Tasks for Lesson 1

B. Task: Division Facts (URG p. 13)

With a partner, use your *Triangle Flash Cards* to quiz each other on the division facts for the threes, nines, and the 12 related division facts for the last six multiplication facts (4×6, 4×7, 4×8, 6×7, 6×8, 7×8). One partner covers the corner with a square with his or her thumb. This number will be the answer to a division fact, called the quotient. The second person divides the two uncovered numbers. Repeat the process, this time covering the corner with a circle.

Each time through the cards, separate them into three piles: those facts you know and can answer quickly, those that you can figure out with a strategy, and those that you need to learn. Practice the last two piles again and then make a list of the facts you need to practice at home for homework.

Circle the facts you know and can answer quickly on your *Division Facts I Know* chart.

D. Task: Computing Multiplication and Division (URG p. 14)

Use paper and pencil or mental math to compute the following. Estimate the answers to see if your answers are reasonable.

1. A. $33 \times 74 =$ B. $50 \times 80 =$

    C. $61 \times 36 =$ D. $27 \times 95 =$

    E. $273 \div 8 =$ F. $1056 \div 6 =$

2. Explain your estimation strategy for Question 1D.

Suggestions for Teaching the Lesson

Math Facts

*   DPP Task B reminds students to use their *Triangle Flash Cards* to practice the division facts for the threes, nines, and last six facts.

*   Part 1 of the Home Practice reminds students to practice division facts using their *Triangle Flash Cards* at home. Part 2 provides fact practice with multiplication tables and fact families.

Answers for Part 2 of the Home Practice can be found in the Answer Key at the end of this lesson and at the end of this unit.

Homework and Practice

*   Assign **Questions 1–5** in the Homework section in the *Student Guide.* Students will need a piece of *Centimeter Graph Paper* to complete the assignment.

*   DPP Bit A provides practice with finding probabilities using plant growth as a context. Bit C reviews time and angle measurement. Task D provides computation practice with multiplication and division.

Name _____   Date _____

Unit 15: Home Practice

Part 1 *Triangle Flash Cards: 3s, 9s, Last Six Facts*

Study for the two quizzes on the division facts. Half the facts will be on the first quiz. The other half will be on the second quiz. Take home your *Triangle Flash Cards* and your list of facts you need to study.

Here's how to use the flash cards. Ask a family member to choose one flash card at a time. Your partner should cover the corner with a square. This number will be the answer to a division fact. Divide the two uncovered numbers. Go through cards again, but this time cover the number in the circle.

Your teacher will tell you when the quizzes on the facts will be. Remember to study only those facts you cannot answer correctly and quickly.

Part 2 **Mixed-Up Multiplication Tables**

1. Complete the tables.

A.

×	3	4	6	7	8
4					
6			24		
7					
8					

B.

×	0	1	5	7	9
3					
6			30		
9					
10					

2. Solve each fact. Then, on a separate sheet of paper, name three other facts that are in the same fact family. For example, the following four facts are in the same fact family: $3 \times 6 = 18$, $6 \times 3 = 18$, $18 \div 3 = 6$, and $18 \div 6 = 3$. (Remember, the square numbers only have two facts in each family.)

A. $8 \times 4 =$ _____   B. $81 \div 9 =$ _____   C. $7 \times 6 =$ _____

D. $9 \times 4 =$ _____   E. $21 \div 7 =$ _____   F. $10 \times 9 =$ _____

G. $3 \times 3 =$ _____   H. $56 \div 7 =$ _____   I. $6 \times 9 =$ _____

USING PATTERNS   DAB · Grade 4 · Unit 15 **239**

Discovery Assignment Book - Page 239

Assessment

Observe students as they plot their data on *Centimeter Graph Paper* and answer the questions about the graph. Record your observations on the *Observational Assessment Record*.

Use this lab to assess students' graphing skills. Grade students' graphs based on the following criteria:

1. Does the graph have a title?

2. Are the axes scaled correctly and labeled clearly? Did they plot Time (*T*) on the horizontal axis and Height (*H*) on the vertical axis? Labeling should be consistent with the picture and the data table and should include appropriate units of measure. (Time in days and height in cm.)

3. Are the points plotted correctly?

4. Did the student draw a smooth curve through the data points?

5. Did the student draw any interpolation or extrapolation on the graph?

Encourage students to write a full explanation of their answers to *Question 11, 14,* or *15* by reviewing the Student Rubric: *Telling.* Score students' work using the Telling dimension of the *TIMS Multidimensional Rubric.*

Extension

- Ask students to answer the following questions that deal with the average growth for all the plants in the class:

  1. Collect data from your classmates. Record the height of their plants at the end of the experiment. Fill in a data table like the one shown in Figure 9.

  2. What is the mean height for all the plants in the class at the end of the experiment? Was your plant's final height higher than, lower than, or close to the mean compared to those of your classmates?

  3. Find the median height for all the plants at the end of the experiment. Is the median height close to the mean height?

Name	Ending Height in cm
Grace	13
Irma	16

Figure 9: *Data table for extension*

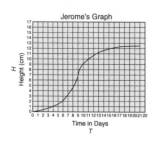

Jerome's Graph

Homework

You will need a piece of *Centimeter Graph Paper.*

1. Grace planted a sunflower seed. She waited until it sprouted and measured its height every few days. She measured the plant at the same time each day, 8 A.M. Here is her data table. Make a graph of Height (in cm) versus Time (in days) of her data on *Centimeter Graph Paper.*

Date	*T* Time in Days	*H* Height in cm
10/19	0	0
10/21	2	$\frac{1}{2}$
10/23	4	1
10/26	7	6
10/28	9	10
10/30	11	12
11/2	14	16
11/4	16	18
11/6	18	19
11/9	21	19

2. What was the height of the plant at the end of the experiment?

3. On which days did the plant grow the most?

4. On which days is the graph the steepest?

404 SG · Grade 4 · Unit 15 · Lesson 1   **Plant Growth Conclusion**

Student Guide - Page 404

5. Here is the graph of Professor Peabody's plant growth data.

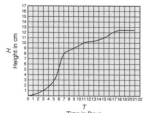

Professor Peabody's mouse, Milo, chewed up his data table. Make a data table like the one below and fill in the missing information using the graph.

T Time in Days	*H* Height in cm
0	
2	0.5
3	
	3
7	
8	
9	
	10
	10.5
19	

Plant Growth Conclusion   SG · Grade 4 · Unit 15 · Lesson 1 405

Student Guide - Page 405

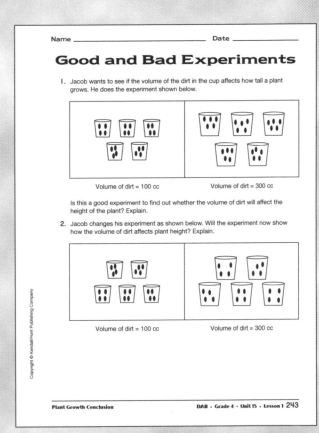

Discovery Assignment Book - Page 243

Suggestions for Teaching the Lesson (*continued*)

- Students can repeat the *Plant Growth* experiment with two different kinds of seeds. They will need to record the information for each plant on a separate data table. After three weeks, they can graph the data they collected and tell which plant grew more or grew faster. Students can then discuss the different growth patterns and rates.

- Students can try other related experiments where they manipulate the amount of light each seed gets, the volume of soil each seed gets, the number of seeds planted, or even the quantity of water given.

Science Connection

This extension can be completed during science time. In the questions on the *Good and Bad Experiments* Activity Page in the *Discovery Assignment Book,* students find errors in the design of an experimental setup and suggest correct ways to design an experiment. In **Question 1,** Jacob did not hold the number of seeds per cup fixed. In **Question 2,** Jacob correctly sets up the experiment. Jacob kept the number of seeds fixed. When he tripled the amount of dirt in each cup, the amount of dirt per seed also tripled.

AT A GLANCE

Math Facts and Daily Practice and Problems

DPP Bit A reviews probability. Task B reminds students to use the *Triangle Flash Cards* to review division facts. Bit C reviews angle measurement. Task D provides multiplication and division practice.

Developing the Lab

1. Students collect data on the growth of a plant using the instructions in Unit 13 Lesson 5.

2. Review the main variables in the *Plant Growth* lab using students' pictures of the experiment, the sample student picture on the *Plant Growth Conclusion* Lab Pages in the *Student Guide,* and *Questions 1–3.*

3. Students plot their data and fit a smooth curve through the points on *Centimeter Graph Paper. (Question 4)*

4. Students complete *Questions 5–12* using data from their tables and graphs.

5. Students complete *Questions 13–15* in class. Students use the Student Rubric: *Telling* to guide their work.

6. Use the *Good and Bad Experiments* Activity Page in the *Discovery Assignment Book* as a science connection.

Homework

1. Assign homework *Questions 1–5* in the *Student Guide.*

2. Assign Parts 1 and 2 of the Home Practice.

Assessment

1. Use students' completed graphs and the *Observational Assessment Record* to note their abilities to make and interpret point graphs.

2. Score students' responses to *Questions 11, 14,* and *15* using the Telling dimension of the *TIMS Multidimensional Rubric.*

Notes:

Student Guide

Questions 1–15 (SG pp. 402–404)

1. *time in days

2. *height in centimeters

3. *type of plant, type of soil, size of container, time of day that the plant is measured, etc.

4.–5. *See Figures 6 and 8 in Lesson Guide 1 for sample student graphs.

6. *Answers will vary. See Content Note, Plant Growth Curves, in Lesson Guide 1. Most plants give data that lie on a curve that looks like a stretched-out "S."

Answers for *Questions 7–12* will vary. The sample answers provided for *Questions 7–12* are based on the sample graphs in Figures 6 and 8 in Lesson Guide 1.

7. 7 cm (Figure 6); $1\frac{1}{2}$ cm (Figure 8)

8. Day 6 (Figure 6); Day 9 (Figure 8)

9. between 13 and 14 cm (Figure 6); 19 cm (Figure 8)

10. A. *The curve is steepest on the days that the plant is growing the fastest.

    B. The curve levels off.

11. *

12. *Answers will vary. The graph in Figure 6 might show continued growth (at the same rate as it has been growing since day 10) for a few more days before it starts leveling off. The graph in Figure 8 might continue to show that the growth rate has leveled off; the growth may in fact stop altogether.

13. *Graph B

14. The graphs in *Bouncing Ball* (Unit 5 Lesson 4) and *Downhill Racer* (Unit 10 Lesson 4) were straight lines, whereas the *Plant Growth* graph is a curve. The graph in Unit 6 Lesson 2 which represents the increase of rice on a checkerboard was a curve which kept increasing. It did not level off, whereas the *Plant Growth* curve does.

15. *Answers will vary. Some possible student responses are in Lesson Guide 1.

Homework (SG pp. 404–405)

Questions 1–5

1. *See the graph in Figure 8 in the Lesson Guide.

2. 19 cm

3. Between day 6 and 8 the plant grew about 6 cm.

4. Between days 6 and 8. In general, on the days the plant grows faster, the graph is steeper.

5.

T Time in Days	H Height in cm
0	0
2	0.5
3	1
5	3
7	8
8	8.5
9	9
11	10
14	10.5
19	12.5

*Answers and/or discussion are included in the Lesson Guide.

**Answers for all the Home Practice in the *Discovery Assignment Book* are at the end of the unit.

Discovery Assignment Book

**Home Practice (DAB p. 239)

Part 2. Mixed-Up Multiplication Tables

Questions 1–2

I. A.

×	3	4	6	7	8
4	12	16	24	28	32
6	18	24	36	42	48
7	21	28	42	49	56
8	24	32	48	56	64

B.

×	0	1	5	7	9
3	0	3	15	21	27
6	0	6	30	42	54
9	0	9	45	63	81
10	0	10	50	70	90

2. **A.** $8 \times 4 = 32$; $4 \times 8 = 32$;
$32 \div 8 = 4$; $32 \div 4 = 8$

B. $81 \div 9 = 9$; $9 \times 9 = 81$

C. $7 \times 6 = 42$; $6 \times 7 = 42$;
$42 \div 7 = 6$; $42 \div 6 = 7$

D. $9 \times 4 = 36$; $4 \times 9 = 36$;
$36 \div 9 = 4$; $36 \div 4 = 9$

E. $21 \div 7 = 3$; $21 \div 3 = 7$;
$7 \times 3 = 21$; $3 \times 7 = 21$

F. $10 \times 9 = 90$; $9 \times 10 = 90$;
$90 \div 9 = 10$; $90 \div 10 = 9$

G. $3 \times 3 = 9$; $9 \div 3 = 3$

H. $56 \div 7 = 8$; $56 \div 8 = 7$;
$7 \times 8 = 56$; $8 \times 7 = 56$

I. $6 \times 9 = 54$; $9 \times 6 = 54$;
$54 \div 9 = 6$; $54 \div 6 = 9$

Good and Bad Experiments (DAB p. 243)

Questions 1–2

1. no; the number of seeds per cup is not held fixed

2. yes; the amount of dirt per seed tripled, the number of seeds is fixed

---

*Answers and/or discussion are included in the Lesson Guide.

**Answers for all the Home Practice in the *Discovery Assignment Book* are at the end of the unit.

OPTIONAL LESSON

There are no Daily Practice and Problems items for this lesson.

In the Shade of the Old Meranpi Tree

Estimated Class Sessions: 1

Dr. Clark and her son Todd travel to Borneo to study how much light certain trees need to grow. They cut down trees which allows more light to reach the rain forest floor in some places. Then, they measure seedlings. They discover that the shade-providing trees, nervosa and macaranga, grow best when a small amount of light is let through. These trees then shade the meranpi and allow it to grow. This information is then used to decide how big a gap can be cut without permanently damaging the rain forest.

TIMS Tip

This story should be read after Lesson 1, the *Plant Growth Conclusion* lab.

Key Content

- Collecting and organizing data.
- Connecting mathematics and science to real-world events: investigating the relationship between light and plant growth.

Key Vocabulary

canopy
clear-cut
gap

germinate
seedlings

Materials List

Print Materials for Students

	Optional Activity
Adventure Book	*In the Shade of the Old Meranpi Tree* Pages 91–106

Student Book

⊙ *available on Teacher Resource CD*

All Transparency Masters, Blackline Masters, and Assessment Blackline Masters in the Unit Resource Guide are on the Teacher Resource CD.

Materials for the Teacher

Transparency of *Two-column Data Table* (Unit Resource Guide, Generic Section), optional
map or globe, optional

Before the Activity

Create two-column data tables on transparencies or on the chalkboard before reading the story. As Dr. Clark and her son create data tables and gather data in the story, keep track of their data.

Discussion Prompts

You may want to read the whole story to students first before going back and using some of the discussion prompts.

Page 92

* *Has anyone ever heard of or traveled to Borneo? Locate Borneo on a map or globe.*

Adventure Book - Page 92

Page 93

* *Locate the tropical rain forest zone, Brazil, and the Congos on the map.*

Discuss with students where other rain forests are found including those found in the Northwestern United States.

Adventure Book - Page 93

Adventure Book - Page 94

Adventure Book - Page 96

Discussion Prompts

Page 94

- *Why are Dr. Clark and Todd studying what happens to the rain forest?*

Each year, more and more of the rain forest is cut down. Many important plants grow in the rain forest. For example, medicines are sometimes made from plants in the rain forest. As more and more rain forest is cut down, the environment changes, causing some plants and animals to die and even become extinct.

- *What animals, insects, and plants live in a rain forest?*

Many different kinds of plants and animals live in the rain forest. Students may remember reading Adventure Books about the rain forest with animals such as armadillos, spider monkeys, and howler monkeys. Students may enjoy reading some of the books listed in the Literature Connections to find out about other animals, insects, and plants that live in the rain forest.

Page 96

- *What are Dr. Clark and Todd going to study?*

Dr. Clark and Todd are going to look at the effects of gaps in the rain forest. They will observe how large of a gap can be cut and still have the rain forest grow back.

- *How does the meranpi cut off 98% of the light?*

The meranpi forms a canopy with its leaves and branches. This canopy blocks off 98% of the light. Students may need to be reminded that 100% is all the light and 98% is very close to 100%.

Discussion Prompts

Page 97

• *How might Dr. Clark and Todd get more light to the meranpi seedlings so they can grow?*

Dr. Clark and Todd might cut down some of the meranpi trees to make a hole in the canopy. This will allow more light to reach the rain forest floor in some places.

• *What else must Dr. Clark and Todd consider when they think about getting more light to the seedlings?*

Dr. Clark and Todd must also consider moisture. If they allow too much light to the rain forest floor, they will cause the seedlings to dry out. They have to find the right amount of light and moisture. You can discuss how Dr. Clark and Todd can make their experiment more reliable by measuring and recording the amount of light and moisture in each gap. However, since the gaps are all in the same region, they should have similar light and moisture levels.

Adventure Book - Page 97

Page 98

Discuss with students that there are several fixed, manipulated, and responding variables. Include in your discussion the idea of multiple trials. Students should realize that for Dr. Clark's study to be reliable, there would have to be several gap sites of each size. Remind students of how they complete several trials in experiments to eliminate as much experimental error as possible.

Adventure Book - Page 98

Adventure Book - Page 99

Adventure Book - Page 100

Discussion Prompts

Page 99

- *Why are Dr. Clark and Todd cutting down two trees at one site, then four trees at another site?*

Dr. Clark and Todd are trying to find a balance between the amount of light let in and the moisture of the ground. The proper balance will allow the plants to grow.

- *How large would you expect the gap to be where they cut down two trees? Four trees?*

Since the gap is about 200 square meters with one tree cut down, the gap should be about 400 square meters with two trees cut down. The gap should be about 800 square meters with four trees cut down.

Page 100

- *Why does Dr. Clark want to measure seedling height vs. time?*

Dr. Clark wants to know how the plants grow with different amounts of sunlight. Seedling height vs. time will tell how much each plant grows over certain periods of time.

Discussion Prompts

Page 101

- *How is Dr. Clark's experiment like your* Plant Growth *experiment?*

Students' answers will vary. Some may make the connection between charting plant growth over time. There are three data tables at the 200-meter gap site. Type of tree and gap size are fixed variables for each data table. Dr. Clark is actually performing nine experiments here, one for each type of tree at each size gap site.

- *Why do you think Dr. Clark and Todd selected* T = *14, 28, and 42 in their data tables?*

Dr. Clark and Todd are collecting data every two weeks. $T = 14, 28$, and 42 shows two-week increments.

- *What do you think Dr. Clark and Todd will do with the information in their data tables?*

They might plot the data on a graph and analyze the results. It will tell them which gap size is best for the trees to grow. Environmental groups and loggers can use this information to help decide how many trees they can cut in one spot without doing too much damage to the plant or animal life in the rain forest.

Page 102

- *In what lab did we gather data similar to the data about the orangutan?*

Arm Span vs. Height in Unit 1.

Adventure Book - Page 101

Adventure Book - Page 102

Adventure Book - Page 103

Adventure Book - Page 104

Discussion Prompts

Page 103

- *What do you think will happen at the 400-square-meter gap site?*

Turn the page and find out.

Page 104

- *If all the trees did not grow well at the 400-square-meter gap site, what do you think might have happened at the 800-square-meter gap site?*

Discussion Prompts

Page 106

You may wish to discuss the complexity of issues raised in the story. Gap cutting gives plants and trees a greater chance to regenerate with less harm to the rain forest than clear cutting the forest. But, in order to cut gaps in the rain forest, loggers must make many trails into the forest to remove the logs. These trails require many trees to be cut down. The benefits of gap cutting versus clear cutting are still under study.

Adventure Book - Page 106

Suggestions for Teaching the Lesson

Homework and Practice

Students can take the *In the Shade of the Old Meranpi Tree* Adventure Book home to share with their families.

Literature Connections

- Baptista, Lynne Hardie. *Discover Rain Forests.* Publications International, Ltd., Lincolnwood, IL, 1993.
- Cherry, Lynne. *The Great Kapok Tree: A Tale of the Amazon Rain Forest.* Voyager Books, New York, 2000.
- Jordan, Martin and Janis. *Journey of the Red-Eyed Tree Frog.* Simon & Schuster, New York, 1992.
- Perez, Ed. *A Look Around Rain Forests.* Willowisp Press, Inc., St. Petersburg, FL, 1993.

Resource

Brown, Nick, and Malcolm Press. "Logging Rain Forests the Natural Way?" in *The New Scientist,* pp. 25–29, IPC Magazines, London, England, 1992.

LESSON GUIDE

Planet Gzorp

Estimated Class Sessions: **2**

Students determine growth patterns for creatures on an imaginary planet called Gzorp. They examine the number patterns that arise in this context. The patterns studied include squaring a number and multiplying by a constant. They use these patterns to tell what the creatures will look like at certain ages and to find the age of a given creature.

Key Content

* Identifying and extending patterns.
* Representing patterns using words, data tables, graphs, and symbols.
* Using patterns to make predictions and solve problems.
* Connecting geometric and number patterns.
* Investigating and using square roots.

Daily Practice and Problems:
Bits for Lesson 3

E. Multiplying and Dividing by Multiples of 10 (URG p. 15)

A. $500 \times 30 =$	B. $60 \times 4 =$
C. $50 \times 90 =$	D. $0 \times 300 =$
E. $2400 \div 8 =$	F. $900 \div 9 =$
G. $30 \div 10 =$	H. $1800 \div 2 =$
I. $210 \div 30 =$	J. $1200 \div 40 =$
K. $60 \times 700 =$	L. $0 \div 9 =$

G. Fact Families for × and ÷
(URG p. 16)

Solve each fact. Then, name the three other facts that are in the same fact family. (The square numbers only have two facts in each family.)

A. $6 \times 8 =$	B. $18 \div 6 =$
C. $81 \div 9 =$	D. $9 \times 8 =$
E. $4 \times 7 =$	F. $3 \times 2 =$
G. $32 \div 4 =$	H. $7 \times 6 =$
I. $9 \div 3 =$	J. $27 \div 3 =$
K. $9 \times 1 =$	

DPP Tasks are on page 51. Suggestions for using the DPPs are on page 51.

Curriculum Sequence

Before This Unit

In Unit 6 Lesson 2 *Doubles,* students explored patterns in data tables with doubles and powers of two.

After This Unit

Students will solve a similar open-response problem as an assessment in Unit 16 Lesson 4 *The Many-Eyed Dragonfly.*

Materials List

Print Materials for Students

	Math Facts and Daily Practice and Problems	Activity	Homework	Written Assessment
Student Books — Student Guide		*Planet Gzorp* Pages 406–410	*Planet Gzorp* Homework Section Page 410	
Student Books — Discovery Assignment Book			Home Practice Parts 3 & 4 Page 240	
Teacher Resources — Facts Resource Guide	DPP Items 15E & 15G			
Teacher Resources — Unit Resource Guide	DPP Items E–H Pages 15–17			*Make Your Own* Pages 54–55, 1 per student
Teacher Resources — Generic Section		*Two-column Data Table,* 4 per student pair		

available on Teacher Resource CD

All Transparency Masters, Blackline Masters, and Assessment Blackline Masters in the Unit Resource Guide are on the Teacher Resource CD.

Supplies for Each Student Pair

calculator
30–35 square-inch tiles

Materials for the Teacher

Observational Assessment Record (Unit Resource Guide, Pages 9–10 and Teacher Resource CD)
Gzorp Rules Transparency Master (Unit Resource Guide) Page 53
Transparency of *Two-column Data Table* (Unit Resource Guide, Generic Section)
overhead square-inch tiles, optional

Developing the Activity

Part 1. Rules and Patterns

Use the *Gzorp Rules* Transparency Master and the first page of the *Planet Gzorp* Activity Pages in the *Student Guide* to introduce students to planet Gzorp and the creatures that live there. Creatures on Gzorp grow each year by adding more squares. They have rules as to how they grow. They only grow by adding squares that match edge to edge or touch corner-to-corner. Creating rules for how Gzorp creatures grow provides a framework for students when they make their own creatures on the *Make Your Own* Assessment Pages.

A one-year-old, a two-year-old, and a three-year-old Add Three Gator are shown on the second *Planet Gzorp* Activity Page. An Add Three Gator has three squares when it is 1 year old. It grows by adding three squares each year. Encourage student pairs to explore Add Three Gators using square-inch tiles. Students can make an Add Three Gator and challenge their partner to tell how old it is. They can reverse the process and ask their partner to make a certain-year-old Add Three Gator.

Not Acceptable

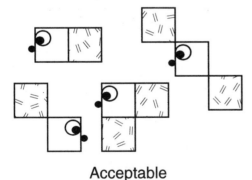

Acceptable

Figure 10: *Rules for Gzorp creatures*

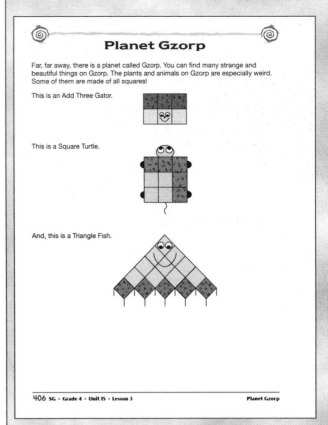

Planet Gzorp

Far, far away, there is a planet called Gzorp. You can find many strange and beautiful things on Gzorp. The plants and animals on Gzorp are especially weird. Some of them are made of all squares!

This is an Add Three Gator.

This is a Square Turtle.

And, this is a Triangle Fish.

406 SG · Grade 4 · Unit 15 · Lesson 3   Planet Gzorp

Student Guide - Page 406

Add Three Gator

The plants and animals that are made of squares grow by adding more squares. Different kinds of plants and animals add squares differently. For example, a 1-year-old Add Three Gator looks like this:

When it is 2 years old, it looks like this:

When it is 3 years old, it looks like this:

It keeps growing, getting three squares larger each year. The dark blue squares show the squares it grows each year.

1. Create a data table like the one below showing the age in years and the size in squares for Add Three Gators between the ages of 1–7.

Add Three Gator Growth

Age in Years	Size in Squares
1	3
2	
3	
4	

2. Do you think an Add Three Gator that is as old as you is very big? Find out. Record the data for this Add Three Gator in your data table.

Student Guide - Page 407

---

3. Use your data table to find out how many squares a 6-year-old Add Three Gator has.

4. How many squares does an 11-year-old Add Three Gator have? Tell how you solved this problem.

5. How old is an Add Three Gator that has 66 squares? Tell how you solved this problem.

6. If an Add Three Gator has 100 squares, about how old is it? Tell how you solved this problem.

Square Turtle

A Square Turtle grows into a bigger square each year. These are 1-, 2-, and 3-year-old Square Turtles.

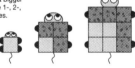

7. A. Draw a 4-year-old Square Turtle.
   B. Write the number of squares it has in all.
   C. How many squares does it have on one side?

8. A. How many squares does a Square Turtle have on one side when it is 5 years old?
   B. How many squares does a 5-year-old Square Turtle have in all?

9. A. Create a data table for Square Turtles between the ages of 1–10.
   B. Describe patterns you see in the table.

Square Turtle Growth

Age in Years	Size in Squares
1	1
2	
3	
4	

Student Guide - Page 408

After some initial exploration, direct students' attention to **Question 1** on the *Planet Gzorp* Activity Pages. Help students start their data tables by charting the growth pattern for the 1, 2, 3, and 4-year-old Add Three Gator on a transparency of a *Two-column Data Table.* Have students create their own data tables as shown in Figure 11. Students may need to build each Add Three Gator with square-inch tiles to complete the table. Encourage them to discuss any patterns they see as they complete the table.

Add Three Gator Growth

Age in Years	Size in Squares
1	3
2	6
3	9
4	12

Figure 11: *A sample data table*

Then, direct students' attention to **Question 2.** Encourage them to solve the problem by continuing to add entries to their data tables. Ask:

- *Describe in words how the creature grows.*

They might say:

- The Add Three Gator grows by multiples of three.
- Each year, it adds three squares.
- You can tell the number of years by dividing the total number of squares by three.

Have students solve **Questions 3–6.** Make calculators available for students' use.

Students solve **Question 6** in a variety of ways. Some use tools such as division, the calculator's constant feature, the data table, or pictures. Others use patterns. The answer to **Question 6** is not a whole number of years. If the Add Three Gator had 99 squares, it would be 33 years old. But, since it has 100 squares, the Add Three Gator is between 33 and 34 years old. Students can either estimate the answer as 33 years, say the age is between 33 and 34 years old, or give the answer of $33\frac{1}{3}$ years. Discuss their solution strategies.

Part 2. Square Turtle

Show students the Square Turtles on the *Planet Gzorp* Activity Pages. Encourage them to complete **Questions 7–8** with little assistance from you. Students should also generate a data table for the Square Turtle as directed in **Question 9.** Discuss patterns found in students' tables. Ask them to describe how a Square Turtle grows. Students may notice that each year, the Square Turtle grows by matching the number of squares it has on each of two sides, then adds one for the corner. See Figure 12.

One-Year-Old

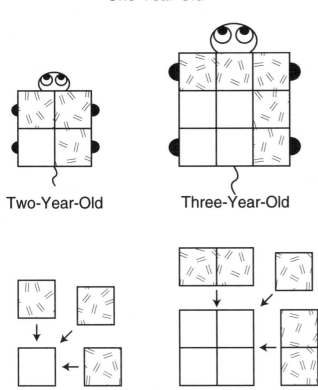

Two-Year-Old   Three-Year-Old

Figure 12: *Square Turtle growth pattern*

Some students may notice that the number of squares added each year is odd (e.g., the two-year-old added 3 squares, the three-year-old added 5 squares, etc.). Others may also notice that a Square Turtle is a square where the age is shown by the number of squares along one side. If n is the number of squares on one side, the total number of squares for any age Square Turtle is $n \times n$ or n^2. Have students complete **Question 10.**

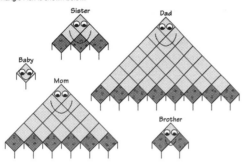

10. How many squares would a 22-year-old Square Turtle have on one side?

11. A. If a Square Turtle has 36 squares, how old is it?
    B. If a Square Turtle has 169 squares, how old is it?

12. A. How many squares does a 10-year-old Square Turtle have?
    B. How many squares does a 75-year-old Square Turtle have? Tell how you know.

13. Estimate the age of a Square Turtle that has 1000 squares.

Triangle Fish

A Triangle Fish is a sea creature on Planet Gzorp. It lives in families. A family of Triangle Fish is shown below.

14. How old are the children in the Triangle Fish family?

15. How old are the parents?

Student Guide - Page 409

Content Note

A **square root** is the length of a side of a square with an area of a given number. The symbol for square root is $\sqrt{}$.
$5 \times 5 = 25; \sqrt{25} = 5$

If students have scientific calculators, they can use them to learn about square numbers and square roots.

To square a number such as 5, students can press:

or

To find the square root, students can use the following keystrokes:

or

Question 11 asks students to tell how old Square Turtles are that have 36 and 169 squares. This is an excellent opportunity to introduce students to square roots. Students should know that to find the number of squares in a Square Turtle for a certain age, they multiply the number of squares on one side by itself. For example, a 5-year-old has five squares on one side, so the total number of squares it has is $5 \times 5 = 5^2 = 25$ squares. Then, ask students how they can find the number of squares on one side of a Square Turtle if it has 25 squares. Students need to find out how many squares it has on one side, or the square root of 25. Students can search for the answer to ***Question 11*** by guessing and checking numbers on their calculators.

Square roots will help students complete ***Question 13.*** Have them discuss methods for estimating the answer to ***Question 13.*** Guess and check is an appropriate method. ***Question 13*** does not have a whole number answer. The age of a Square Turtle that has 1000 squares is between 31 and 32 years old.

Part 3. Triangle Fish

Introduce students to the Triangle Fish on the *Planet Gzorp* Activity Pages. The growth pattern for the Triangle Fish may not be immediately apparent to students. Ask students to observe the pictures of the Triangle Fish growth on their activity pages. Students should see that the children are 1, 2, and 3 years old and the adults are 6 and 8 years old (*Questions 14–15*).

Ask students to build Triangle Fish of various ages and chart the growth in a data table (*Question 16*). A sample data table is shown in Figure 13.

Triangle Fish Growth

Age in Years	Size in Squares
1	1
2	3
3	6
4	10

Figure 13: *Triangle Fish sample data table*

Discuss any patterns that students may find. Students may notice that:

- The Triangle Fish grows the number of squares that it ages for each year. For example, a 2-year-old Triangle Fish grows two squares when it turns 2 years old.

- The size in squares of a Triangle Fish is equal to its size from the previous year plus its age in years. For example, the total number of squares for a 4-year-old Triangle Fish is the number of squares it had when it was 3 years old (6) plus its age (4) for a total of 10 squares.

- A Triangle Fish is similar to half of a Square Turtle. If you put a Triangle Fish together with a Triangle Fish that is one year younger, you will get a square. See Figure 14.

- The number of squares a Triangle Fish has can be found by adding all the whole numbers from one to the age of the fish. For example, the size of a four-year-old Triangle Fish is $1 + 2 + 3 + 4 = 10$ squares.

The last two descriptions are very important and may help students solve many of the problems that follow. Demonstrate the relationship between the Triangle Fish and the Square Turtle with square-inch tiles at the overhead. Create a three- and a four-year-old Triangle Fish and join their jagged edges to form a Square Turtle as shown in Figure 14. Ask students how many squares are on the side of the Square Turtle. Students should notice that there are four, the age of the older Triangle Fish. You may need to repeat this connection with other ages of Triangle Fish at the overhead until students become familiar with the relationship.

Once students are able to clearly verbalize how a Triangle Fish grows *(Questions 16B),* begin to explore *Questions 17–20.* Ask students to read and discuss strategies for solving *Question 17.* Students must find the number of squares in a ten-year-old and a fifteen-year-old Triangle Fish. One method for finding the number of squares in a fifteen-year-old is to continue the data table until the age is 15 years. If students have articulated how a Triangle Fish grows, they should recognize that another strategy is to add $1 + 2 + 3 + 4 \ldots + 15$. Using calculators, they can quickly find the solution of 120 squares. Encourage students to explore other ways of solving this problem. If students see that a Triangle Fish is about half of a Square Turtle, then they can estimate the solution by squaring 15 (for the number of squares on one side of a fifteen-year-old Square Turtle), then dividing by 2 to find the size of the Triangle Fish: $15^2 = 225$ and $225 \div 2 = 112.5$, or about 110 squares.

---

16. A. Create a data table for Triangle Fish between the ages of 1–10. [*Hint:* A four-, five-, and seven-year-old Triangle Fish are not shown in the family.]
    B. Describe in words how a Triangle Fish grows.

Triangle Fish Growth	
Age in Years	Size in Squares
1	1
2	
3	
4	

17. A. How many squares does a 10-year-old Triangle Fish have?
    B. How many squares does a 15-year-old Triangle Fish have?

18. A. If a Triangle Fish has 36 squares, how old is it?
    B. If a Triangle Fish has 210 squares, how old is it?
    C. If a Triangle Fish has 465 squares, how old is it?

19. How could you find out how many squares there are in a 48-year-old Triangle Fish? Estimate the answer.

20. Estimate the age of a Triangle Fish that has 20,100 squares.

Homework

You will need a calculator to complete this homework.

1. How many squares does a 30-year-old Add Three Gator have? Show your work.

2. Estimate the age of an Add Three Gator that has 5000 squares. Tell how you made your estimate.

3. How many squares are on one side of a Square Turtle that has 81 squares in all?

4. How many squares does a Square Turtle have on each side if it has 361 squares in all?

5. How many squares does a 30-year-old Square Turtle have? Show your work.

6. Estimate the age of a Square Turtle that has 7500 squares. Tell how you made your estimate.

7. Estimate the number of squares a 25-year-old Triangle Fish has.

410 SG · Grade 4 · Unit 15 · Lesson 3   Planet Gzorp

Student Guide - Page 410

Three-Year-Old Triangle Fish + Four-Year-Old Triangle Fish = A Square Turtle with four squares on each side

Figure 14: *Joining Triangle Fish to make a square*

Question 18 asks students to do the reverse: to find the age of a Triangle Fish when given the number of squares. They can read the solution to *Question 18A* directly from their tables and can find the solution to *Question 18B* by extending their tables. Some students may choose to solve *Question 18B* by adding consecutive numbers on their calculators until the sum of 210 is reached $(1 + 2 + 3 \ldots + 20 = 210)$. Since the last value entered is 20, a Triangle Fish made of 210 squares is 20 years old. You may want students to make estimates by using the half of a Square Turtle method. To estimate the answer to *Question 18C,* they first double 465, then take the square root: $2 \times 465 = 930$ and the square root of 930 is between 30 and 31 years old. So, the age of a Triangle Fish with 465 squares is about 30 years old. (It is in fact actually 30 years old.)

Questions 19–20 are challenging problems. It is unlikely that students would extend their data tables or keep adding up on the calculator to solve these problems. They will have to estimate. You may want to chart some of the estimates and have students see what the trend is for estimates. Encourage students to tell how they got their estimates. An exact solution to these problems is not important. What is important is that students are able to make reasonable estimates and defend their processes for making their estimates. The simplest way to find a good estimate for *Question 20* is to use the idea that a Triangle Fish is about half of a Square Turtle. Students would have to double the number of squares to make a Square Turtle, then take the square root. This leads to an estimate of about 200 or 201 years old. The exact solution to this problem is 200 years.

Suggestions for Teaching the Lesson

Math Facts

DPP Bits E and G provide math facts practice. Bit E practices multiplying and dividing with multiples of 10. Bit G uses fact families to practice the division facts for the threes, nines, and last six facts.

Homework and Practice

- Assign the Homework section in the *Student Guide.* Students answer questions about the Gzorp creatures they explored in class. Encourage them to use their data tables and calculators to answer the questions.

- DPP Task F asks students to identify patterns. Task H provides computation practice with division.

- Assign Parts 3 and 4 of the Home Practice. Part 3 provides computation practice and Part 4 reviews elapsed time.

Answers for Parts 3 and 4 of the Home Practice can be found in the Answer Key at the end of this lesson and at the end of this unit.

Assessment

- Assign the *Make Your Own* Assessment Blackline Master. Remind students of the rules for Gzorp creatures using the *Gzorp Rules* transparency. Observe students as they create Gzorp creatures. If students have difficulty getting started, ask them to think of a number pattern first, then model it with the tiles. You might check students' creatures in Year 1 and Year 2 to make sure that they are on the right track. This will prevent them from having difficulties completing the remaining problems. Use the *Observational Assessment Record* to record students' abilities to identify and extend patterns.

- Unit 16 Lesson 4 *The Many-Eyed Dragon Fly* is an assessment problem that uses Gzorp creatures. Students must identify the growth pattern for a new Gzorp creature and use the pattern to solve problems. You may choose to complete this assessment at this time.

Extension

Post students' *Make Your Own* Assessment Blackline Master on a bulletin board. Encourage students to observe the work posted, then try to solve the problems for the various plants and creatures.

Daily Practice and Problems:
Tasks for Lesson 3

F. Task: Add to the Pattern (URG p. 15)

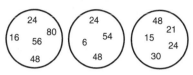

1. What do the numbers in each circle have in common? Write two more numbers that belong in each circle.

2. Why are 24 and 48 in all three circles?

H. Task: Division Practice
(URG p. 17)

Use paper and pencil or mental math to compute the following. Estimate to see if your answers are reasonable.

1. $87 \div 3 =$ 2. $417 \div 5 =$

3. $247 \div 6 =$ 4. $4916 \div 9 =$

5. $5984 \div 8 =$ 6. $6078 \div 7 =$

Name _____ Date _____

Part 3 Practicing the Operations

On a separate sheet of paper, solve the following problems using paper and pencil or mental math. Estimate to make sure your answers are reasonable.

1. A. $546 + 89 =$ _____   B. $3438 - 723 =$ _____
   C. $2905 + 376 =$ _____   D. $79 \times 5 =$ _____
   E. $2306 \times 8 =$ _____   F. $347 \div 5 =$ _____
   G. $62 \times 40 =$ _____   H. $5073 - 782 =$ _____
   I. $9540 \div 6 =$ _____   J. $504 \div 9 =$ _____
   K. $1789 + 4532 =$ _____   L. $6730 - 762 =$ _____
   M. $29 \times 44 =$ _____   N. $4003 \div 7 =$ _____

2. Explain your strategy for Question 1D.

Part 4 Telling Time

1. What time is it? _____

2. What time will it be in 3 hours? _____

3. What time was it 45 minutes ago? _____

4. What time will it be in $1\frac{1}{2}$ hours? _____

5. What time was it 90 minutes ago? _____

6. Jacob's grandmother is coming to Chicago for a visit. Her plane takes off in Florida at 11:30 A.M. It will take her about 45 minutes to get to the airport. If she wants to arrive at the airport about $1\frac{1}{2}$ hours before take-off, what time should she leave her home?

7. Irma's brother is in high school. He has four 55-minute classes before lunch. If his first class starts at 8:05 and there are 5 minutes between each class, what time is his lunch period? Show how you decided.

Discovery Assignment Book - Page 240

AT A GLANCE

Math Facts and Daily Practice and Problems

DPP Bits E and G provide math facts practice. Task F explores patterns. Task H provides division practice.

Part 1. Rules and Patterns

1. Introduce students to creatures from Planet Gzorp using the first page of the *Planet Gzorp* Activity Pages in the *Student Guide.*
2. Using the *Gzorp Rules* transparency, tell students the rules for how a Gzorp creature can grow.
3. Students discuss the growth pattern for an Add Three Gator and find ways to tell the number of squares it has at a certain age.
4. Students create a data table charting the growth pattern for an Add Three Gator *(Question 1).*
5. Students complete *Questions 2–6* in the *Student Guide.*

Part 2. Square Turtle

Students explore the growth pattern for a Square Turtle by completing *Questions 7–13* in the *Student Guide.*

Part 3. Triangle Fish

1. Students explore and discuss the growth pattern for a Triangle Fish using square-inch tiles.
2. Students complete *Questions 14–16* in the *Student Guide.* They create a data table and articulate how a Triangle Fish grows.
3. Students discuss strategies and make estimates while completing *Questions 17–20.*

Homework

1. Assign the Homework section in the *Student Guide.*
2. Assign Parts 3 and 4 of the Home Practice.

Assessment

1. Use the *Make Your Own* Assessment Blackline Masters to assess students' abilities to make and extend patterns. Record observations on the *Observational Assessment Record.*
2. Ask students to complete the open-response problem in Unit 16 Lesson 4 to assess students' growth in solving problems and communicating solutions.

Notes:

Gzorp Rules

Not Acceptable

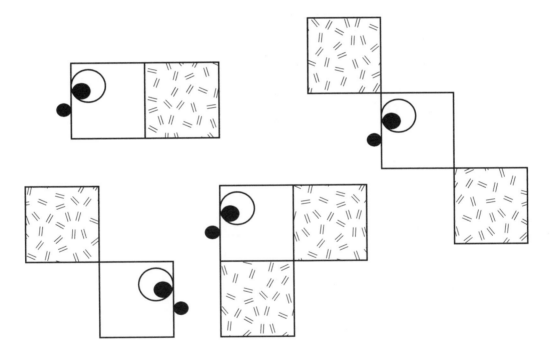

Acceptable

Make Your Own

Make up your own plant or animal from planet Gzorp. Show how it grows.

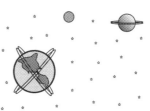

Year 1	Year 2
Year 3	**Year 4**

1. Name your plant or animal. _____

2. Complete the data table for your plant or animal.

Age in Years	Size in Squares
1	
2	
3	
4	
5	
6	

3. Describe how the pattern in your data table grows.

4. Fill in the blanks to make up three questions about how your plant or animal grows. Write your answers on a separate piece of paper.

A. How many squares does a _____ year old _____ have?
name of
animal or plant

B. One of my _____ has _____ squares. How old is it?
name of
animal or plant

C. My _____ is _____ years old. How many squares will it have?
name of
animal or plant

D. Make up your own problem.

Student Guide

Questions 1–20 (SG pp. 407–410)

1. Add Three Gator Growth

Age in Years	Size in Squares
1	3
2	6
3	9
4	12
5	15
6	18
7	21

2. Answers will vary. An Add Three Gator that is eight years old has 24 squares. An Add Three Gator that is nine years old has 27 squares. An Add Three Gator that is ten years old has 30 squares.

3. 18 squares

4. 33 squares. Solution strategies will vary. Students can multiply 11 years × 3 squares per year = 33 squares.

5. 22 years old. Solution strategies will vary. Students can divide 66 squares ÷ 3 squares per year = 22 years.

6. *Between 33 and 34 years old or $33\frac{1}{3}$ years old. Solution strategies will vary. Students can divide 100 squares ÷ 3 squares per year = $33\frac{1}{3}$ years.

7. A.

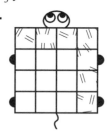

    B. 16 squares

    C. 4 squares

8. A. 5 squares

    B. 25 squares

9. A.   Square Turtle Growth

Age in Years	Size in Squares
1	1
2	4
3	9
4	16
5	25
6	36
7	49
8	64
9	81
10	100

    B. *

10. 22 squares

11. A. *6 years old

    B. 13 years old

12. A. 100 squares

    B. 5625 squares. Students' solution strategies will vary. A Square Turtle that is 75 years old has 5625 squares because it is a square with 75 squares on a side. (75 × 75 = 5625)

13. *Estimates will vary. The actual solution is between 31 and 32 years old.

14. 1, 2, and 3 years old

15. 6 and 8 years old

*Answers and/or discussion are included in the Lesson Guide.

**Answers for all the Home Practice in the *Discovery Assignment Book* are at the end of the unit.

16. A.   Triangle Fish Growth

Age in Years	Size in Squares
1	1
2	3
3	6
4	10
5	15
6	21
7	28
8	36
9	45
10	55

   B. *

17. A. 55 squares
    B. *120 squares
18. A. *8 years old
    B. *20 years old
    C. *30 years old
19. *Estimates will vary. The actual solution is 1176 squares.
20. *Estimates will vary. The actual solution is 200 years.

Homework (SG p. 410)

Questions 1–7

1. 90 squares. $30 \times 3 = 90$.
2. Estimates will vary. Students need to divide 5000 by 3. The actual solution is between 1666 and 1667 years.
3. 9 squares
4. 19 squares
5. 900 squares. $30 \times 30 = 900$.
6. Estimates will vary. The actual solution is between 86 and 87 years.
7. Estimates will vary. The actual solution is 325 squares.

Discovery Assignment Book

**Home Practice (DAB p. 240)

Part 3. Practicing the Operations

Questions 1–2

1. A. 635
   B. 2715
   C. 3281
   D. 395
   E. 18,448
   F. 69 R2
   G. 2480
   H. 4291
   I. 1590
   J. 56
   K. 6321
   L. 5968
   M. 1276
   N. 571 R6

2. Possible strategy: $80 \times 5 = 400$; $400 - 5 = 395$.

Part 4. Telling Time

Questions 1–7

1.–5. Answers will vary depending on the time given in *Question 1*.
6. 9:15 A.M.
7. Lunch starts at 12:00 P.M. or 12:05 P.M. His first class is from 8:05 to 9:00. His second class is from 9:05 to 10:00. His third class is from 10:05 to 11:00. His fourth class is from 11:05 to 12:00.

Unit Resource Guide

Make Your Own (URG pp. 54–55)

Questions 1-4

1.–4. Solutions will vary based on the creatures students create.

**Answers and/or discussion are included in the Lesson Guide.
****Answers for all the Home Practice in the *Discovery Assignment Book* are at the end of the unit.

Daily Practice and Problems: Bits for Lesson 4

I. Find the Pattern (URG p. 17)

1. Draw the next two shapes on *Centimeter Grid Paper*.

2. How many square centimeters will there be in each shape?

K. Planet Gzorp (URG p. 18)

On Planet Gzorp there is a family of six L-gators. The three female L-gators are 3 years old, 14 years old, and 29 years old. The three males are 9, 18, and 41 years old.

1. What is the mean age of the members of this family of L-gators?

2. What is the median age?

DPP Tasks are on page 62. Suggestions for using the DPPs are on page 62.

LESSON GUIDE 4
Function Machines

Estimated Class Sessions: 2–3

This activity introduces students to functions through the activity *Guess My Rule.* Students use function machines to generate an "output" number for every "input" number. They record their findings in data tables and explore different ways to describe the patterns or rules generated by function machines.

Key Content

- Identifying and extending patterns.
- Representing patterns and functions using words, symbols, and data tables.
- Expressing mathematical relationships using variables.

Key Vocabulary

function machine
input
output

Materials List

	Math Facts and Daily Practice and Problems	Activity	Homework	Written Assessment
Student Books				
Student Guide		*Function Machines* Pages 411–414	*Function Machines* Homework Section Pages 415–416	
Discovery Assignment Book				Home Practice Part 6 Page 242
Teacher Resources				
Facts Resource Guide ⊙	DPP Items 15J & 15L			
Unit Resource Guide	DPP Items I–L Pages 17–19 ⊙			
Generic Section ⊙	*Centimeter Grid Paper,* 1 per student	*Two-column Data Table,* 8 per student		

⊙ *available on Teacher Resource CD*

All Transparency Masters, Blackline Masters, and Assessment Blackline Masters in the Unit Resource Guide are on the Teacher Resource CD.

Supplies for Each Student

calculator

Materials for the Teacher

Transparency of *Two-column Data Table* (Unit Resource Guide, Generic Section)

Student Guide - Page 411

Function Machines

Irma and Luis are exploring their Auntie Pat's attic one day.

Irma: "Hey, Luis, look at this!"
Luis: "It looks like some kind of machine."

Irma: "Yeah, but what is it?"

Irma: "It says Double Machine. What do you think that means?"
Luis: "Maybe it doubles stuff."

Irma: "Look at all these cards with numbers on them. They look as though they fit in the slot."
Luis: "Let's try it!"

They put in a card with 25 on it and turned the crank. With a lot of coughing, sputtering, and choking, the machine spits out a card saying 50.

Irma: "It really works!"
Luis: "This machine could help us double all kinds of numbers."

Function Machines   SG · Grade 4 · Unit 15 · Lesson 4 411

Student Guide - Page 411

Student Guide - Page 412

1. Irma and Luis tried the double machine on lots of numbers. They put their results in a data table like the one below. Make a data table like this one and fill in the blank spaces.

Doubling Machine

Input	Output
25	50
7	14
14	
	30
100	
	100
	7
N	2 × N

Luis: "Say, Irma, I found another machine over here, but I can't read the label."
Irma: "Let's try it out and see if it works."

Luis: "I put in 10 and out came 20."
Irma: "It looks like another doubling machine. Let's put in 20."

Luis: "30 came out, so it can't be doubling."

412 SG · Grade 4 · Unit 15 · Lesson 4   Function Machines

Student Guide - Page 412

Developing the Activity

To set the stage for the activity, read the story of Irma and Louis in the *Function Machines* Activity Pages in the *Student Guide.*

Encourage students to explore doubles with the Doubling Machine *(Question 1).* Use a transparency of the *Two-column Data Table* to organize the information. Label the columns of the data table Input and Output. Complete the data table by having students tell you certain numbers to double, then record what the machine would do. A sample data table for the Double Machine is shown in Figure 15. Note that the first blank entry asks for the output when the input is 14. In other words, what is double 14? On the next line we are given the output (30) and are asked for the input. In other words, what is the number whose double is 30? Some students may require trial and error to find the answer to this problem, while others will see that the input number must be half of the output number.

Doubling Machine

Input	Output
25	50
7	14
14	
	30
100	
	100
	7
N	2 × N

Figure 15: *A data table for the Doubling Machine (from* Student Guide*)*

For large numbers, students can use their calculators to find the output. For example, ask,

- *If 673 is the input, then what is the output?* (This is a good opportunity for estimation. Note that there is more than one way to do this on a calculator. Students might add $673 + 673$ or they might multiply by 2: 2×673.)

Continue the *Student Guide* vignette leading to an exploration of the Add 10 Function Machine (*Questions 2–4*). Discuss how to describe function machines in words and using symbols.

Questions 5–6 provide practice with two more function machines. The function machine in *Question 5* uses the rule "Multiply by 10 and Subtract 5."

Question 6 is a Subtract 5 Function Machine. If students completed the optional Lesson 6 in Unit 3 *What's Below Zero?*, they can use this function machine to explore negative numbers. They can extend the table below zero by naturally following the pattern of the numbers. Each number in the right-hand column is five less than the corresponding number in the left-hand column. As you go down each column, the numbers in both columns decrease by 1. Figure 16 shows an extended table with negative numbers.

Input	Output
12	7
11	
	5
9	
	3
	2
6	
	0
N	N − 5
4	−1
3	−2
2	
1	
0	

Figure 16: *"Subtract 5" Function Machine extended to negative numbers*

Have students work in pairs or small groups to play *Guess My Rule* following the rules in the *Student Guide.* Interesting function machines can be displayed on a bulletin board. Students will play this game at home with their family members for homework.

---

2. Make a data table like the one below and fill in the missing entries.

Mystery Machine

Input	Output
10	20
20	30
5	15
17	27
	45
25	
0	
	39
N	

3. What does the mystery machine do? There are many ways to answer this question. You can write the answer in words: The mystery machine is an "add ten machine."

You can write the answer in symbols. If we use *N* to stand for the Input number, then:

$$\text{Output} = N + 10$$

4. If you are given an output number, how can you find the input number?

Student Guide - Page 413

Here are two more function machines. The one in Question 5 multiplies the input number by 10 and then subtracts 5. The machine in Question 6 subtracts 5 from the input number. Set up two-column data tables like the ones below and fill in the missing values.

5.

Input	Output
1	5
2	15
3	25
4	35
	55
15	
	205
100	
N	10 × N − 5

6.

Input	Output
12	7
11	
	5
9	
	3
	2
6	
	0
N	N − 5

Guess My Rule

This is a game for two or more players. The players will need a *Two-column Data Table.* They can use calculators if they like.

- One player is the Function Machine. The player thinks of a rule and writes it down on a piece of paper but doesn't tell it to the other players.
- The other players take turns, each one giving the Function Machine an input number and writing it in the data table. The player who is the Function Machine tells the other players the output number and writes it in the data table.
- A player may make one guess describing the rule during his or her turn.
- The first player to guess the rule is the winner. In the next round the winner becomes the Function Machine.

Student Guide - Page 414

Conclude this lesson by making the connection between function machines and the previous lessons in the unit. For example, the data tables we made in the Gzorp lesson can be thought of as function machines. To be specific, we can make an Add Three Gator Function Machine. When the input is N, the output is the number of squares in an N-year old Add Three Gator or $N \times 3$.

Function machines can be used to describe the results of some experiments. The input is the manipulated variable and the output is the responding variable. For example, if I am growing a plant, I can design a *Plant Growth* Function Machine for my plant. For an input number t, the output is the height of my plant after t days.

Suggestions for Teaching the Lesson

Math Facts

DPP Task J provides practice with multiplication facts, order of operations, and function machines. Task L uses related number sentences to divide with multiples of 10.

Homework and Practice

- Assign the Homework section in the *Student Guide.* This section introduces students to more function machines. *Question 6* asks students to play *Guess My Rule* with a family member.

- DPP Bit I provides practice identifying and extending patterns. Bit K reviews mean and median.

- Remind students to continue practicing the division facts for the threes, nines, and last six facts using their *Triangle Flash Cards.*

Daily Practice and Problems:
Tasks for Lesson 4

J. Task: Function Machine: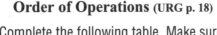
Order of Operations (URG p. 18)

Complete the following table. Make sure you follow the correct order of operations.

Input	Output
1	
2	
3	
4	
5	
6	
7	
N	$10 + 3 \times N$

L. Task: Related Multiplication
and Division Sentences (URG p. 19)

Find a number for n in each number sentence that makes the statement true.

1. $4 \times n = 2400$ $2400 \div 4 = n$

2. $n \times 9 = 360$ $360 \div 9 = n$

3. $7 \times n = 63{,}000$ $63{,}000 \div 7 = n$

4. $6 \times n = 54$ $54 \div 6 = n$

5. $9 \times n = 4500$ $4500 \div 9 = n$

6. $8 \times n = 560$ $560 \div 8 = n$

7. $3 \times n = 0$ $0 \div 3 = n$

Assessment

Use Home Practice Part 6 as an assessment of students' abilities to represent functions with symbols and data tables.

Answers for Part 6 of the Home Practice can be found in the Answer Key at the end of this lesson and at the end of this unit.

Name _____ Date _____

Part 6 Function Machines

1. Complete each data table using the rules provided.

A.

Input N	Output 8 × N − 4
1	4
3	
5	
7	
9	
11	

B.

Input N	Output 50 − N × 2
2	46
4	
6	
8	
10	
12	

C.

Input N	Output 7 × N + 2
4	
6	
8	
	72

D.

Input N	Output 9 × N
5	
	63
	72
	90

2. Find the rule for each function machine. Then, find the missing numbers in each of the tables.

A.

Input N	Output ___
11	5
15	9
23	17
	27
	53
100	

B.

Input N	Output ___
4	80
5	100
	140
9	180
	200
30	

USING PATTERNS

Discovery Assignment Book - Page 242

In Questions 1–2, use the Input-Output Patterns to complete each data table.

1.

Input	Output
3	10
10	
	27
53	
	200
	1000
100	
N	N + 7

2.

Input	Output
1	30
2	
3	
4	
5	
10	120
	100
N	10 × N + 20

Here are data tables for two function machines. Find the Input-Output patterns. Use the patterns to fill in the blanks in each data table. Describe the Input-Output patterns using words or symbols (or both).

3.

Input	Output
1	12
2	24
3	
4	48
5	
10	
	240
N	

4.

Input	Output
20	41
15	31
10	
	11
0	
2	5
	101
N	

Student Guide - Page 415

---

5. Make a data table like this on your paper. Make up your own values for the input and output columns which follow a rule. Write the rule in symbols in the last row.

Input	Output
N	

6. Play *Guess My Rule* with a family member.

Student Guide - Page 416

AT A GLANCE

Math Facts and Daily Practice and Problems

DPP items I and J provide practice with patterns. Bit K reviews median and mean. Task L practices math facts and division with multiples of 10.

Developing the Activity

1. Introduce the lesson by beginning the story about Irma and Luis on the *Function Machines* Activity Pages in the *Student Guide.*

2. Model the double machine *(Question 1)* with a transparency of the *Two-column Data Table.*

3. Continue the story.

4. Explore the Add 10 Function Machine. Discuss how to describe function machines using words and symbols. *(Questions 2–4)*

5. Explore the Multiply by 10 and Subtract 5 machine in *Question 5.*

6. In *Question 6,* students can explore negative numbers by completing the pattern in a Subtract 5 Function Machine. (optional)

7. Have each student make his or her own data table and have other students guess the rule.

8. Discuss the connections between the data tables in Gzorp, the data tables in the labs, and function machines.

Homework

1. Assign the Homework section in the *Function Machines* Activity Pages in the *Student Guide.*

2. Students practice division facts using the *Triangle Flash Cards.*

Assessment

Use Home Practice Part 6 as an assessment.

Notes:

Student Guide

Questions 1–6 (SG pp. 412–414)

1. *

Doubling Machine

Input	Output
25	50
7	14
14	28
15	30
100	200
50	100
3.5	7
N	$2 \times N$

2.

Mystery Machine

Input	Output
10	20
20	30
5	15
17	27
35	45
25	35
0	10
29	39
N	$N + 10$

3. *It adds 10 to the input number.

4. Subtract 10 from the output number.

5.

Input	Output
1	5
2	15
3	25
4	35
6	55
15	145
21	205
100	995
N	$10 \times N - 5$

6. *

Input	Output
12	7
11	6
10	5
9	4
8	3
7	2
6	1
5	0
N	$N - 5$

*Answers and/or discussion are included in the Lesson Guide.

**Answers for all the Home Practice in the *Discovery Assignment Book* are at the end of the unit.

Homework (SG pp. 415–416)

Questions 1–6

1.

Input	Output
3	10
10	17
20	27
53	60
193	200
993	1000
100	107
N	N + 7

2.

Input	Output
1	30
2	40
3	50
4	60
5	70
10	120
8	100
N	10 × N + 20

3.

Input	Output
1	12
2	24
3	36
4	48
5	60
10	120
20	240
N	N × 12

4.

Input	Output
20	41
15	31
10	21
5	11
0	1
2	5
50	101
N	2 × N + 1

5.–6. Answers will vary.

*Answers and/or discussion are included in the Lesson Guide.

**Answers for all the Home Practice in the *Discovery Assignment Book* are at the end of the unit.

Discovery Assignment Book

**Home Practice (DAB p. 242)

Part 6. Function Machines

Questions 1–2

1. **A.**

Input N	Output 8 × N − 4
1	4
3	20
5	36
7	52
9	68
11	84

B.

Input N	Output 50 − N × 2
2	46
4	42
6	38
8	34
10	30
12	26

C.

Input N	Output 7 × N + 2
4	30
6	44
8	58
10	72

D.

Input N	Output 9 × N
5	45
7	63
8	72
10	90

2. **A.**

Input N	Output N − 6
11	5
15	9
23	17
33	27
59	53
100	94

B.

Input N	Output N × 20
4	80
5	100
7	140
9	180
10	200
30	600

*Answers and/or discussion are included in the Lesson Guide.

**Answers for all the Home Practice in the *Discovery Assignment Book* are at the end of the unit.

LESSON GUIDE 5

Taste of TIMS

Estimated Class Sessions: 2–3

Students find the mass of a sandwich using a two-pan balance. They then see how the mass changes as bites are taken out of the sandwich. A discussion in the *Student Guide* helps students explore the distinction between mass and weight.

Key Content

- Identifying and using variables.
- Measuring mass.
- Collecting, organizing, graphing, and analyzing data.
- Making and interpreting point graphs.
- Connecting mathematics and science to real world events: measuring mass.
- Telling the story of a graph.
- Using patterns to make predictions.

Key Vocabulary

grams
mass
massing

Curriculum Sequence

Before This Unit

Mass. Students explored mass concepts in Grade 2 Unit 8 and Grade 3 Unit 9.

Materials List

Print Materials for Students

		Math Facts and Daily Practice and Problems	Lab	Homework	Written Assessment
Student Books	**Student Guide**		*Taste of TIMS* Pages 417–423 and Student Rubric: *Telling:* Appendix C and Inside Back Cover ⊙	*Taste of TIMS* Homework Section Page 423	
	Discovery Assignment Book			Home Practice Part 5 Page 241	
Teacher Resources	**Facts Resource Guide** ⊙	DPP Items 15M & 15O			DPP Item 15M *Division Facts Quiz 1* and DPP Item 15O *Division Facts Quiz 2*
	Unit Resource Guide	DPP Items M–P Pages 19–21 ⊙	*Mass Review* Pages 79–81, 1 per student (optional)		DPP Item M *Division Facts Quiz 1* Page 19 and DPP Item O *Division Facts Quiz 2* Page 20 ⊙
	Generic Section ⊙		*Two-column Data Table,* 1 per student and *Centimeter Graph Paper,* 2 per student		

⊙ available on Teacher Resource CD

All Transparency Masters, Blackline Masters, and Assessment Blackline Masters in the Unit Resource Guide are on the Teacher Resource CD.

Supplies for Each Student

sandwich
piece of napkin, plastic wrap, or wax paper
calculator

Supplies for Each Student Group

set of standard masses
two-pan balance

Materials for the Teacher

Graphing Mistakes: What's Wrong Here? Transparency Master (Unit Resource Guide) Page 78
Transparency of *Two-column Data Table* (Unit Resource Guide, Generic Section), optional
Transparency of *Centimeter Graph Paper* (Unit Resource Guide, Generic Section), optional
TIMS Multidimensional Rubric (Teacher Implementation Guide, Assessment section and Teacher Resource CD)
Observational Assessment Record (Unit Resource Guide, Pages 9–10 and Teacher Resource CD)
Individual Assessment Record Sheet (Teacher Implementation Guide, Assessment section and Teacher Resource CD)
sandwich for demonstration
napkin, plastic wrap, or wax paper
set of standard masses
two-pan balance

Masses of Common Objects

Object	Mass in Grams
calculator	81
unused pencil	5
unused piece of chalk	11
unused eraser	38
small scissors	19
12-inch plastic ruler	10
wooden meterstick	109
hexagon pattern block	11.5
trapezoid pattern block	6
square pattern block	3

Figure 17: *Masses of some common objects*

Before the Lab

Remind students to bring in sandwiches for the experiment. Sandwiches must be whole, not sliced in halves or quarters. The filling for sandwiches does not matter. But each sandwich must be composed of two slices of bread with a filling of some sort. You might want to pack a few extra sandwiches in case students forget to bring them.

If students are not familiar with finding the mass of objects, they should complete the *Mass Review* Blackline Masters in the *Unit Resource Guide* prior to the laboratory investigation. To assist students in becoming proficient in massing objects, set up stations throughout the classroom with objects for students to mass. Approximate masses of some objects found in one typical classroom are shown in Figure 17.

The *Mass Review* Activity Pages remind students how to zero their balances and compare masses with and without standard masses. Students mass objects and record their mass in data tables *(Question 1)*. Then, they answer questions about the data they gathered.

The questions on the *Mass Review* Activity Pages allude to the possibility of measurement error. Students should realize reasons for measurement error include the limitations in the accuracy of the measurement instrument and skill of the experimenters. For example, the smallest mass in your set of standard masses will probably be one gram. So, measurements can only be accurate to the nearest gram. Also, school kits of standard masses may not be very precise. See the TIMS Tutor: *Estimation, Accuracy, and Error* in the *Teacher Implementation Guide* for more information.

Discuss the possibility of measurement error with your students. Encourage them to compare their data for the stations set up throughout the room.

Questions 2–3 ask students to identify the object with the least and the most mass. The answers to these questions will vary depending upon the objects students choose to mass. Students can either use their data tables to solve this problem, or they can compare the masses of the objects against one another using the two-pan balance. In the table in Figure 17, the wooden meterstick has the most mass and the square pattern block has the least mass.

Question 4 asks students to compare the object with the most mass to the object with the least mass. Students can compare the objects by saying that one object has about twice or three times the mass of the other, that one object has more mass than the other, or they may simply state the difference in the masses. Students should check the reliability of their data by placing each object on opposite sides of the two-pan balance and adding masses to the side with the least mass until the objects balance. Students can then compare the difference in their data tables to the difference on the balance. For example, if the masses of the wooden meterstick and the square pattern block in the table above were compared, they would have a difference of 106 grams. In theory, adding 106 grams to the lighter side of the balance should balance the two pans. However, this may not happen due to experimental error. The difference of their masses on the balance could be 108 grams. Ask students to account for this discrepancy. The discrepancy may occur because a different wooden meterstick or square pattern block was used in the original data collection, the balance was not properly zeroed, because of rounding due to the limitations of the measurement tool, or inaccuracy of the standard masses.

Questions 5–7 explore the additive property of mass. Namely, the mass of two objects together is the sum of their individual masses. In practice, this may not work out exactly due to the possibility of experimental error. Students should base their predictions on the masses listed in their data tables and then check the reliability with a balance. Encourage students to discuss why any error may have occurred. Then, ask students to come up with solutions for dealing with experimental error. Students may remember collecting data for multiple trials in previous labs. Lead them to the idea that measuring the mass of an object several times, then taking the mean or median mass, can help minimize experimental error. If students measure carefully, then their predictions should not be off by more than 1 or 2 grams.

Developing the Lab

Part 1. Gravity, Mass, and Weight

In second and third grade of this curriculum, students explored the distinction between mass and weight. *Math Trailblazers* encourages students to use their own familiar language when dealing with mass. For example, students may not be familiar with the term "massing" and may say that they are "weighing" objects instead of "massing" them. Traditionally, we use a two-pan balance to find the mass of an object and a spring scale (e.g., a bathroom scale) to weigh an object. For more information regarding mass, refer to the TIMS Tutor: *The Concept of Mass* in the *Teacher Implementation Guide.*

Taste of TIMS

Weight and Mass

Professor Peabody is having trouble telling the difference between weight and mass. He knows that **mass** is the amount of matter in an object and that **weight** is a measure of the pull of gravity. But, it's hard to tell the difference on Earth. So, he decides to travel to the moon to see what happens to his weight and mass.

Professor Peabody weighs 148 pounds on Earth. He discovers that his **weight** on the moon is less than his weight on the Earth. Why do you think this happens?

The moon's gravity is weaker than the Earth's. Because there is less gravity pulling on Professor Peabody, he has less weight.

Taste of TIMS   SG · Grade 4 · Unit 15 · Lesson 5   417

Student Guide - Page 417

Now, he checks his mass.

His **mass** has stayed the same! Why do you think this has happened? Why didn't Professor Peabody's mass change when the gravity changed?

Student Guide - Page 418

Taste of TIMS

Shannon used the sandwich she brought for lunch to do an experiment. She placed her sandwich on a two-pan balance and used standard masses to find its mass. Then, she took a bite out of her sandwich and found the mass of the remaining sandwich. Shannon kept taking bites out of her sandwich, each time finding the mass, until her sandwich was gone.

Repeat Shannon's experiment using a sandwich of your own.

Draw a picture of the experiment.

1. What is the manipulated variable?
2. What is the responding variable?
3. What variable or variables are fixed during the experiment?

Student Guide - Page 419

Ask students to read the Weight and Mass section of the *Taste of TIMS* Lab Pages in the *Student Guide.* Students should already be aware of the differences in gravity on the Earth and the moon from news about space travel or from displays at museums and planetariums. Discuss each of the questions on these activity pages in preparation for completing the lab.

On the first page, Professor Peabody travels to the moon and finds that his weight is different on the moon. He weighs less on the moon than on Earth. There is less gravity on the moon than on the Earth. And since **weight** is the force of gravity on a certain mass and there is less gravitational force on the moon, Professor Peabody has less weight. The weight of an object is a measure of the "pull" of gravity on the object. Since there is less gravity on the moon, Professor Peabody weighs less.

The second activity page shows students how Professor Peabody's mass did not change between the Earth and the moon. Professor Peabody has the same **mass,** the same amount of matter as he did on Earth. The pull of gravity has changed, but not the mass. Professor Peabody can measure his mass on the moon, provided he uses a balance. He balances the same number of standard masses as he did on Earth. The weaker pull of gravity does not matter since it is a weaker pull on both Professor Peabody and the standard masses.

Part 2. Gathering and Organizing the Data

The directions for this lab are written fairly sparsely. We hope that at this time in the year, students should be able to "take the directions and run with them." Discuss and model the lab's general process, then let student pairs try to complete the lab independently. If your students are not prepared to do this, you will need to provide more direction than is suggested in this guide. You may want to remind students of the TIMS Laboratory Method before beginning this laboratory investigation.

Each student will first find the mass of a whole sandwich, then take a bite and mass the sandwich again. They repeat the process for one, two, and four bites. Students may want to take large bites out of their sandwiches. However, this will decrease their opportunities to collect data. Encourage them to take normal-size bites, all the same size. This makes "size of bites" a fixed variable and results in a better pattern in the data. Students with bites of equal size will be more able to make accurate predictions.

After the lab's general process is established, discuss how to organize the data that will be collected.

Students should record their data in a table using a *Two-column Data Table.* They can follow the lab's general process on the *Taste of TIMS* Lab Pages in their *Student Guides.*

Questions 1–3 ask students to draw a picture of the experiment and name the variables. You can assess students' readiness to begin data collection by reviewing students' pictures and their answers to *Questions 1–3.* The manipulated variable is the number of bites taken while the responding variable is the mass of the remaining sandwich in grams. Examples of fixed variables are the person taking the bites, the kind of sandwich, and the size of the bite.

Each student will have a sandwich to mass, so pairs will have to complete the data collection twice, once for each of their sandwiches. A sample data table for *Question 4* is shown in Figure 18.

After completing the data table, students graph their results on *Centimeter Graph Paper.* Make sure that students appropriately label and scale each axis. A sample graph is shown in Figure 19.

Finding the Mass of a Sandwich

N Number of Bites	M Mass (in grams)
0	72
1	64
2	59
4	45

Figure 18: *A sample data table*

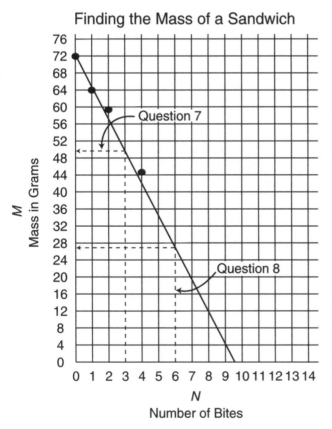

Finding the Mass of a Sandwich

Figure 19: *A sample graph*

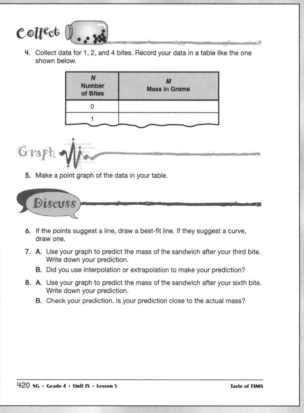

Collect

4. Collect data for 1, 2, and 4 bites. Record your data in a table like the one shown below.

N Number of Bites	M Mass in Grams
0	
1	

Graph

5. Make a point graph of the data in your table.

Discuss

6. If the points suggest a line, draw a best-fit line. If they suggest a curve, draw one.

7. A. Use your graph to predict the mass of the sandwich after your third bite. Write down your prediction.
   B. Did you use interpolation or extrapolation to make your prediction?

8. A. Use your graph to predict the mass of the sandwich after your sixth bite. Write down your prediction.
   B. Check your prediction. Is your prediction close to the actual mass?

420 SG · Grade 4 · Unit 15 · Lesson 5   Taste of TIMS

Student Guide - Page 420

Question 6 asks students to draw a line or curve for the data on their graphs. If the size of the bites are fairly regular, the data should suggest a decreasing line as shown in Figure 19. In general, irregularities in

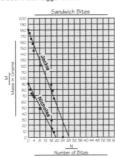
Student Guide - Page 421

---

the data and graphs will be caused by irregularities in the consumption of the sandwich and variations in the size of the bite. If students have sandwiches made with rolls instead of bread slices, fitting a curve through their data points may be more appropriate.

Use the *Graphing Mistakes: What's Wrong Here?* Transparency Master to discuss correct graphing technique. This transparency shows errors in scaling, labeling, and drawing a best-fit line. Ask:

- *Are the axes labeled correctly?* (No, the horizontal axis should read "Number of Bites" and the vertical axis should include the unit of mass—grams.)
- *Are the axes scaled correctly?* (No, the vertical axis is scaled by fours, but goes 20, 24, 30.)
- *Is the best-fit line drawn correctly?* (No, the line does not have a best-fit. There are two data points above the line and none below it.)

Part 3. Exploring the Data

Have students use their data tables and graphs to answer *Questions 7–15* in pairs.

Questions 7–9 ask students to use the data on their graphs to make predictions. Students should be able to use their data table or graph for *Question 7,* but they may have to extend their line to find a point for *Question 8.* In Figure 19, the mass of the sandwich is approximately 50 grams after three bites. Some students may not have a solution for *Question 8* if their data shows that they would have finished eating their sandwich in less than six bites. Knowing this will help them complete *Question 9.* The sample data in Figure 19 shows a sandwich with a mass of approximately 27 grams after six bites, and the best-fit line suggests that it would take ten bites to finish off the sandwich.

Question 10 asks students to find the mean number of grams eaten for their bites. Encourage students to discuss how they might find this solution. One method is to find the mass of each bite and then find the average. For example, if a student's sandwich had a mass of 64 grams after one bite and it had a mass of 72 grams with zero bites, the mass of the bite was 8 grams (72 grams – 64 grams = 8 grams). Students will have to repeat this process until they find the mass of each bite, then sum them, and divide by the number of bites to find the mean. Another way to find the mean mass of each bite is to divide the total mass of the sandwich by the total number of bites. For example, if the total mass of the sandwich was 72 grams and it took you 10 bites of equal size to eat it, then the average mass of each bite is 72 grams ÷ 10 bites = 7.2 grams per bite.

Encourage students to complete **Question 11** with their partners. Students can use a different color to plot their partner's data. **Question 12** asks students to tell who has the bigger bite size. (By bite size, we mean mass of bite.) This may differ from bite to bite. For example, one partner may have a larger bite size for bite number 2, but a smaller bite size for bite number 3. Encourage students to analyze their graphs to find who has the largest mean bite size. Then, students can compare their mean bite sizes found in **Question 10.** In general, the student with the larger bite size will have the steeper graph since each of the larger bites will be plotted further down on the graph. Students may have fun finding out who has the largest mean bite size in the class. Pairs can report their mean bite sizes for a class comparison. You can extend this exploration by finding the smallest bite size in the class or the mean and median bite size for the class.

Encourage students to refer to their graphs when completing **Questions 13–15.** Comparing their partner's results with their own should give them insights into how to complete these questions. For **Question 13**, students can say that the graphs are both straight lines that go downhill. Jackie's sandwich had more mass than Nicholas's to begin with. Each student took about the same size bites (the steepness of the lines are about the same), although since Jackie's line is slightly steeper, she took slightly bigger bites.

In **Question 14,** for graph A, Roberto and Shannon start out with sandwiches that have the same mass (the graphs meet at the vertical axis at the same place), but Shannon takes larger bites (her line is steeper). In graph B, Nila and John start out with sandwiches with different masses, but they take the same-sized bites (the steepness of their lines is the same). In graph C, Romesh began with a larger sandwich and he takes larger bites (his graph crosses the vertical axis higher than Jessie's and his line is steeper).

Question 15 is an excellent lead-in to an extension for this lab. Romesh completed *Taste of TIMS* with an apple instead of a sandwich and got a graph with a different shape. He found that his bites were large at the start, but they got smaller as he neared the core. Since the size of the bites was not constant, his graph is a curve, not a line. And, he never finished eating the apple completely, because he didn't eat the core. Students can repeat the lab using an apple. Then, have them compare the different shaped graphs. Students can tell stories about their bite sizes for different foods.

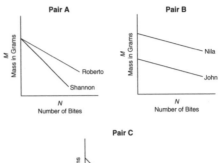

14. Three pairs of students do a similar experiment. They mass a sandwich, then record the mass after one bite, two bites, and four bites have been eaten.
   A. Tell what is the same and different for each graph.
   B. For each pair, what does the graph say about the mass of each sandwich?
   C. For each pair, what does the graph say about the size of the students' bites?

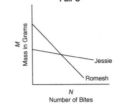

Student Guide - Page 422

15. Romesh did the *Taste of TIMS* lab with an apple. He plotted his data in a graph. Tell a story about the graph.

Homework

You will need a sheet of *Centimeter Graph Paper.*

1. Professor Peabody used the *Taste of TIMS* lab to see how long it took his mouse, Milo, to eat a dish of food. He recorded the data in a table. Plot a graph for Professor Peabody's data.

2. Predict the mass of the food left in the dish after 3 days.

3. Predict how many days it would take Milo to eat the entire dish of food.

4. What is the average amount of food eaten each day? Show how you got your answer.

N Number of Days	M Mass in Grams
0	114
1	103
2	91
4	67
6	43
8	22

Student Guide - Page 423

N. Task: Clean It Up! (URG p. 20)

Frank found a function machine that was so dirty that he couldn't read its rule. He recorded some of the inputs and outputs, but his paper got smudged. Complete Frank's data table. Then, tell the rule for the function machine.

Input	Output
29	2900
■	8000
1290	■
513	51,300

P. Task: Drawing Angles (URG p. 21)

You will need a protractor to complete the following problems.

1. Draw ∠RTG with a measurement of 35°.

2. Draw ∠MQF with a measurement of 115°.

3. Draw ∠GWP with a measurement of 78°.

Name _____ Date _____

Part 5 Solving Problems

Choose an appropriate method to solve each of the following problems. For some questions, you may need to find an exact answer, while for other questions you may need only an estimate. For each question, you may choose to use paper and pencil, mental math, or a calculator. Be prepared to tell the class how you solved each problem.

1. Nila has $585 in her savings account. On her birthday, she deposits $75 that she got for birthday gifts. How much money is in her savings account after her birthday?

2. Jackie and her family are taking a 32-mile ferry ride to an island in Lake Michigan. A round-trip ferry ride ticket costs $29 per adult and $15 per child. If 4 adults and 3 children purchase tickets, how much will the ferry ride cost the entire family?

3. John's older brother is in college. His brother and his three roommates want to buy furniture that costs $764. If they split the cost of the furniture evenly, how much should each student pay?

4. Ming built a house of cards. Before the house came tumbling down, he used 2 full decks of cards. The house also contained all but 15 cards from a third deck. About how many cards were in Ming's house of cards? (A deck of cards has 52 cards.)

5. On vacation, Shannon's family took 3 rolls of 24 pictures and 2 rolls of 36 pictures. How many pictures did the family take in all?

6. Roberto is driving with his family to visit his grandmother. After driving 144 miles from Chicago, the family stops for lunch. They drive 89 more miles and stop for gas. Then, they stop for a soft drink after driving 123 more miles. Roberto's grandma lives 375 miles from Chicago. About how many more miles must they drive before they reach their grandmother's house?

7. If one year is 365 days, how many days old will you be when you are 16 years old?

USING PATTERNS   DAB · Grade 4 · Unit 15 241

Discovery Assignment Book - Page 241

Suggestions for Teaching the Lesson

Homework and Practice

- Assign *Questions 1–4* in the Homework section in the *Student Guide* for homework. Students will need a piece of *Centimeter Graph Paper* to complete *Question 1.*

- DPP Task N uses a function machine to practice multiplication and division with multiples of 10. Task P reviews drawing angles with a protractor.

- Assign some or all of the questions in the *Student Guide* for Lesson 6 *Patterns and Problems* for homework.

- Assign Home Practice Part 5 which is a set of word problems.

Answers for Part 5 of the Home Practice can be found in the Answer Key at the end of this lesson and at the end of this unit.

Assessment

- Observe students as they measure mass. Record your observations on the *Observational Assessment Record.*

- Transfer appropriate documentation from the Unit 15 *Observational Assessment Record* to students' *Individual Assessment Record Sheets.*

- Encourage students to write a full explanation of their answer to *Question 13, 14,* or *15.* Students can use the Student Rubric: *Telling* to guide them as they write. Then, use the Telling dimension of the *TIMS Multidimensional Rubric* to score students' work.

- Follow the guidelines for grading labs in the Assessment section of the *Teacher Implementation Guide.*

- DPP Bits M and O together assess all the division facts for the threes, nines, and last six facts.

Extension

Encourage students to repeat *Taste of TIMS* using an apple. Students should record and organize their data in a table and a graph. Encourage them to compare their graphs from the sandwich and the apple. Then, have them tell the stories of their graphs. The graph for the sandwich will have a best-fit line since the size of students' bites for sandwiches are constant. The graph for the apple will have a curve since the size of the bites of an apple vary (e.g., the first bite might be rather small, the next several bites are large, and the final bites are quite small since the core is reached).

AT A GLANCE

Math Facts and Daily Practice and Problems

DPP Bits M and O are quizzes on division facts. DPP Task N is a function machine. Task P reviews drawing angles.

Part 1. Gravity, Mass, and Weight

1. If students are not familiar with measuring mass, work through the *Mass Review* Blackline Masters.
2. Familiarize students with the distinction between mass and weight with the Weight and Mass section of the *Taste of TIMS* Lab Pages in the *Student Guide.*

Part 2. Gathering and Organizing the Data

1. Discuss and model the lab's general process and review the steps in the TIMS Laboratory Method.
2. Discuss ways to collect the data.
3. Check students' readiness to begin the lab by reviewing their pictures and answers to *Questions 1–3.*
4. Students find the mass of their sandwiches and collect their data using the *Taste of TIMS* Lab Pages as a guide. *(Question 4)*
5. Students graph their data and fit a line or a curve through the points. *(Questions 5–6)*
6. Use the *Graphing Mistakes: What's Wrong Here?* Transparency Master to review correct graphing procedures.

Part 3. Exploring the Data

1. Students examine the shapes of their graphs and compare them to their partner's graphs.
2. Students interpolate and extrapolate using their graphs in *Questions 7–9.*
3. Students compare their data, find mean bite sizes, and explore other data in *Questions 10–15.*

Homework

1. Assign the Homework section on the *Taste of TIMS* Lab Pages.
2. Assign the problems in the *Student Guide* for Lesson 6.
3. Assign Part 5 of the Home Practice.

Assessment

1. Use the *Observational Assessment Record* to rate students' skills measuring mass.
2. Transfer appropriate documentation from the Unit 15 *Observational Assessment Record* to students' *Individual Assessment Record Sheets.*
3. Score students' responses to *Questions 13, 14,* or *15* in the *Student Guide* using the Telling dimension of the *TIMS Multidimensional Rubric.*
4. DPP Bits M and O quiz students on division facts.

Notes:

Graphing Mistakes: What's Wrong Here?

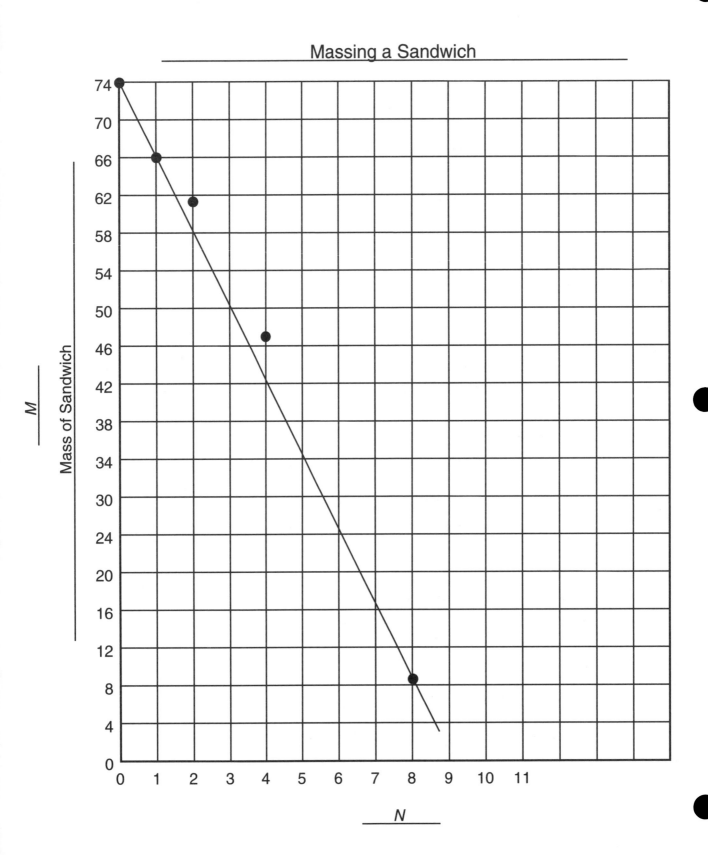

Massing a Sandwich

M — Mass of Sandwich

N

Transparency Master

Mass Review

What is mass?

Mass is the amount of matter in an object. We can get an idea about the mass of an object by lifting it up.

If we want to compare the mass of two things, we can use a two-pan balance. But before we use the balance, we should make sure it is level. You can use a small piece of clay to level your balance by placing it on the side that is higher.

Name _____ Date _____

In order to measure mass, we need a unit of measure. Common metric units of mass are the gram (g) and the kilogram (kg). A kilogram is 1000 grams. So, we measure the mass of small objects in grams and the mass of large objects in kilograms.

We can find the mass of an object using the two-pan balance.

Michael used the two-pan balance to find the mass of his calculator. His standard masses have a mass of 1 gram and 10 grams. He found the mass was 92 grams.

1. Use a two-pan balance to find the mass of at least four objects. Record your results in the data table below.

O Object	*M* Mass (in ____) unit

Use your data to answer the following questions. Sometimes, you will have to collect more data to provide an answer.

2. Which object has the most mass?

3. Which object has the least mass?

Blackline Master

4. Compare the mass of the objects from Questions 2 and 3. Describe how the masses compare, using words or number sentences.

5. Choose any two of your objects, and use your data to predict the total mass of those two objects together.

   A. Write down the mass of each object and your prediction for the total.

   B. Use the balance to find the actual mass of the two objects together.

   C. Was your predicted mass close to the actual mass? How close?

6. A. Put the object with the most mass in one pan. Put the object with the second largest mass in the other pan. Predict how much mass you will have to add to the lighter side to get the pans to balance. Write down your prediction.

   B. Check your prediction by adding mass to the lighter side until the pans balance. Write down the actual number of grams you added to the balance. Is the actual number close to your prediction?

7. Were any of your predictions different from your actual results? On a separate sheet of paper discuss why that might have happened.

Student Guide

Questions 1–15 (SG pp. 419–423)

1. *Number of bites taken

2. *Mass of remaining sandwich in grams

3. *Person taking the bites, kind of sandwich, size of bite, etc.

4. *See Figure 18 in Lesson Guide 5 for a sample data table.

5.–6. *See Figure 19 in Lesson Guide 5 for a sample graph.

Questions 7–10 are answered using the sample graph in Figure 19 in Lesson Guide 5.

7. **A.** *About 50 grams.

    B. Interpolation

8. **A.** *About 27 grams.

    B. Answers will vary.

9. *10 bites

10. *7.2 grams

11. Answers will vary.

12. Answers will vary.

13. *Jackie's sandwich had more mass and she took slightly larger bites.

14. *See Lesson Guide 5 for a description of the graphs.

15. *See Lesson Guide 5 for a story of the graph.

Homework (SG p. 423)

Questions 1–4

1.

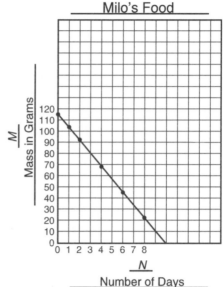

2. About 80 grams

3. About 10 days

4. If it takes 10 days to eat the entire dish of food, then 114 grams in all divided by 10 days is an average of 11.4 grams eaten each day.

Discovery Assignment Book

**Home Practice (DAB p. 241)

Part 5. Solving Problems

Questions 1–7

1. $660   2. $161   3. $191

4. Estimates will vary. One possible estimate is 140 cards ($2 \times 50 + 40$).

5. 144 pictures

6. Estimates will vary. About 20 miles ($145 + 90 + 120$). About 15 miles ($150 + 90 + 120$).

7. 5840 days (365×16; not counting leap years)

Unit Resource Guide

Mass Review (URG pp. 80–81)

Questions 1–7

*1.–7. Answers will vary. See Figure 17 in the Lesson Guide for a sample data table.

---

*Answers and/or discussion are included in the Lesson Guide.

**Answers for all the Home Practice in the *Discovery Assignment Book* are at the end of the unit.

Patterns and Problems

Estimated Class Sessions: 1–2

Students complete a series of word problems that review patterns, function machines, and graphing.

OPTIONAL LESSON

There are no Daily Practice and Problems items for this lesson.

Key Content

*   Identifying and extending patterns.
*   Making and interpreting point graphs.
*   Representing patterns in data tables, graphs, and words.
*   Solving problems involving mass.
*   Identifying and describing situations with varying rates of change.

Materials List

Print Materials for Students

		Optional Activity
Student Book	**Student Guide**	*Patterns and Problems* Pages 424–427
Teacher Resource	**Generic Section** ⊙	*Centimeter Graph Paper,* 1 per student

⊙ *available on Teacher Resource CD*

All Transparency Masters, Blackline Masters, and Assessment Blackline Masters in the Unit Resource Guide are on the Teacher Resource CD.

Supplies for Each Student

calculator

Patterns and Problems

You will need a piece of *Centimeter Graph Paper* and a calculator to complete these problems.

1. Ming's function machine triples a number, then subtracts three. Jackie's function machine doubles a number, then subtracts two.

Machine X	
Input	**Output**
1	0
2	3
3	6

Machine Y	
Input	**Output**
1	0
2	2
3	4

   A. Which data table is Ming's?
   B. Which data table is Jackie's?

2. Maya's and Roberto's function machines have different rules.
   A. Help them complete their data tables for the numbers 0–5.

Double Plus Two	
Input	**Output**
0	
1	
2	

Add 1, Then Double	
Input	**Output**
0	
1	
2	

   B. What do you notice about Maya's and Roberto's data tables? Explain.

Student Guide - Page 424

---

3. Jacob's function machine is missing its rule. Help Jacob find the rule for his function machine.

Input	Output
0	5
1	7
2	9
3	11
4	13
5	15

Give a title for the data table that shows the rule.

4. Nila's sandwich has a mass of 153 grams. She took one bite and the mass of her sandwich is 122 grams.
   A. If each of Nila's bites has the same mass, what is the mass of two bites?
   B. How much mass will three bites have?
   C. How many bites can Nila take until her sandwich is gone?

5. John's sandwich has a mass of 139 grams. He took one bite and the mass of his sandwich is 109 grams.
   A. If each of John's bites has the same mass, how many bites can John take until his sandwich is gone?
   B. Who has a bigger bite size, Nila or John?

Student Guide - Page 425

Developing the Activity

Students solve a series of word problems that practice skills and concepts from this unit. The problems can be used in several ways. Students can work individually, in pairs, or in groups. One approach is to ask students to work on the problems individually at first and then to come together in pairs or small groups to compare solutions. Then each group's solutions can be shared with the others in a class discussion. The problems can also be assigned for homework. Because this activity does not require much teacher preparation, it is appropriate to leave for a substitute teacher.

Suggestions for Teaching the Lesson

Homework and Practice

Assign some or all of the problems for homework.

6. Irma has organized her plant growth data in a table. Plot Irma's plant growth data on *Centimeter Graph Paper*.

Plant Growth

Day	Height (in centimeters)
0	0
4	2
5	4
7	8
8	12
11	14
15	15
17	15

A. How many centimeters did Irma's plant grow by Day 6? Show your work.

B. Use your graph to predict how many centimeters Irma's plant will grow by Day 18.

Patterns and Problems

Student Guide - Page 426

---

7. Frank organized his plant growth data in a table. Plot Frank's plant growth data on the same piece of *Centimeter Graph Paper* as Irma's. Describe the differences and similarities in their graphs.

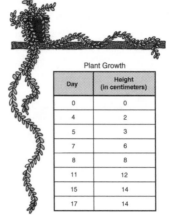

Plant Growth

Day	Height (in centimeters)
0	0
4	2
5	3
7	6
8	8
11	12
15	14
17	14

Student Guide - Page 427

AT A GLANCE

Developing the Activity

Students complete *Questions 1–7* in the *Student Guide* individually or in groups.

Homework

Students complete some or all of the problems for homework.

Notes:

Student Guide

Questions 1–7 (SG pp. 424–427)

1. **A.** Machine X
   B. Machine Y

2. **A.**

   ### Double Plus Two

Input	Output
0	2
1	4
2	6
3	8
4	10
5	12

   ### Add 1, Then Double

Input	Output
0	2
1	4
2	6
3	8
4	10
5	12

   B. The outputs are the same in each table. Doubling and adding two is the same as adding one then doubling.

3. Double Plus Five

4. **A.** 62 grams
   B. 93 grams
   C. 5 bites

5. **A.** 5 bites
   B. Nila

6. **A.** About 6 centimeters
   B. About 15 centimeters

7. Irma's and Frank's graphs are very similar. Both plants grew at about the same rate, but Frank's plant grew a little slower, therefore his plant didn't grow quite as tall.

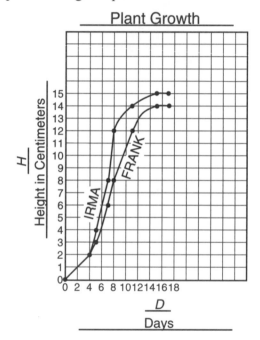

Plant Growth

*Answers and/or discussion are included in the Lesson Guide.
**Answers for all the Home Practice in the *Discovery Assignment Book* are at the end of the unit.

Discovery Assignment Book

Part 2. Mixed-Up Multiplication Tables

Questions 1–2 (DAB p. 239)

I. **A.**

×	3	4	6	7	8
4	12	16	24	28	32
6	18	24	36	42	48
7	21	28	42	49	56
8	24	32	48	56	64

B.

×	0	1	5	7	9
3	0	3	15	21	27
6	0	6	30	42	54
9	0	9	45	63	81
10	0	10	50	70	90

2. **A.** $8 \times 4 = 32$; $4 \times 8 = 32$;
$32 \div 8 = 4$; $32 \div 4 = 8$

B. $81 \div 9 = 9$; $9 \times 9 = 81$

C. $7 \times 6 = 42$; $6 \times 7 = 42$;
$42 \div 7 = 6$; $42 \div 6 = 7$

D. $9 \times 4 = 36$; $4 \times 9 = 36$;
$36 \div 9 = 4$; $36 \div 4 = 9$

E. $21 \div 7 = 3$; $21 \div 3 = 7$;
$7 \times 3 = 21$; $3 \times 7 = 21$

F. $10 \times 9 = 90$; $9 \times 10 = 90$;
$90 \div 9 = 10$; $90 \div 10 = 9$

G. $3 \times 3 = 9$; $9 \div 3 = 3$

H. $56 \div 7 = 8$; $56 \div 8 = 7$;
$7 \times 8 = 56$; $8 \times 7 = 56$

I. $6 \times 9 = 54$; $9 \times 6 = 54$;
$54 \div 9 = 6$; $54 \div 6 = 9$

Part 3. Practicing the Operations

Questions 1–2 (DAB p. 240)

I. **A.** 635   **B.** 2715
C. 3281   **D.** 395
E. 18,448   **F.** 69 R2
G. 2480   **H.** 4291
I. 1590   **J.** 56
K. 6321   **L.** 5968
M. 1276   **N.** 571 R6

2. Possible strategy: $80 \times 5 = 400$;
$400 - 5 = 395$.

Part 4. Telling Time

Questions 1–7 (DAB p. 240)

I.–5. Answers will vary depending on the time given in *Question 1.*

6. 9:15 A.M.

7. Lunch starts at 12:00 P.M. or 12:05 P.M. His first class is from 8:05 to 9:00. His second class is from 9:05 to 10:00. His third class is from 10:05 to 11:00. His fourth class is from 11:05 to 12:00.

Part 5. Solving Problems

Questions 1–7 (DAB p. 241)

I. $660

2. $161

3. $191

4. Estimates will vary. One possible estimate is 140 cards ($2 \times 50 + 40$).

5. 144 pictures

6. Estimates will vary. About 20 miles ($145 + 90 + 120$). About 15 miles ($150 + 90 + 120$).

7. 5840 days (365×16; not counting leap years)

*Answers and/or discussion are included in the Lesson Guide.

Part 6. Function Machines

Questions 1–2 (DAB p. 242)

I. A.

Input N	Output $8 \times N - 4$
1	4
3	20
5	36
7	52
9	68
11	84

B.

Input N	Output $50 - N \times 2$
2	46
4	42
6	38
8	34
10	30
12	26

C.

Input N	Output $7 \times N + 2$
4	30
6	44
8	58
10	72

D.

Input N	Output $9 \times N$
5	45
7	63
8	72
10	90

2. A.

Input N	Output $N - 6$
11	5
15	9
23	17
33	27
59	53
100	94

B.

Input N	Output $N \times 20$
4	80
5	100
7	140
9	180
10	200
30	600

*Answers and/or discussion are included in the Lesson Guide.